HOLT®

ChemFile® A

Skills Practice Experiments
Teacher Guide

HOLT, RINEHART AND WINSTON

A Harcourt Education Company

Orlando • **Austin** • New York • San Diego • Toronto • London

Contents

Ordering Lab Materials with the
One-Stop Planner® CD-ROM

Your class and prep time are valuable. Now, it's easier and faster than ever to organize and obtain the materials that you need for all of the labs in the *Modern Chemistry* lab program. Using the Lab Materials QuickList software found on the *One-Stop Planner® CD-ROM*, you can do the following:

• View all of the materials that you need for any (or all) labs.
The Lab Materials QuickList software allows you to easily see all of the materials needed for any lab in the *Modern Chemistry* lab program. Use your materials list to order all of your materials at once. Or use the list to determine what items you need to resupply or supplement your stockroom so that you'll be prepared to do any lab.

• Create a customized materials list.
No two teachers teach exactly alike. The Lab Materials QuickList software allows you to select labs by type of lab or by type of material used. You can create a materials list that summarizes the needs of whichever labs from *Modern Chemistry* you choose.

• Let the software handle the details.
You can customize your list based on the number of students and the number of lab groups. A powerful software engine that has been programmed to distinguish between consumable and nonconsumable materials will "do the math." Whether you're examining all of the labs for a whole year or just the labs that you're planning for next week, the software does the hard work of totaling and tallying, telling you what you need and *exactly* how much you'll need for the labs that you've selected.

• Print your list.
By printing out materials lists that you created by using the Lab Materials QuickList software, you can have a copy of any materials list right at your fingertips for easy reference at any time.

• Order your materials easily.
After you've created your materials list by using the Lab Materials QuickList software, you can use it to order from Sargent-Welch or to prepare a purchase order to be sent directly to another scientific materials supplier.

Visit go.hrw.com to learn more about the Lab Materials QuickList software.

Teacher's Laboratory Safety Information

HELPING STUDENTS RECOGNIZE THE IMPORTANCE OF SAFETY

One method that can help students appreciate the importance of precautions is to use a safety contract that students read and sign, indicating they have read, understand, and will respect the necessary safety procedures, as well as any other written or verbal instructions that will be given in class. You can find a copy of a safety contract on the *Modern Chemistry One Stop Planner CD-ROM.* You can use this form as a model or make your own safety contract for your students with language specific to your lab situation. When making your own contract, you could include points such as the following:

- Make sure that students agree to wear personal protective equipment (goggles and lab aprons) at all times. Safety information regarding the use of contact lenses is continually changing. Check your state and local regulations on this subject. Students should agree to read all lab exercises before they come to class. They should agree to follow all directions and safety precautions and to use only materials and equipment that you provide.

- Students should agree to remain alert and cautious at all times in the lab. They should never leave experiments unattended.

- Students should not wear dangling jewelry or bulky clothing.

- Students should bring only lab manuals and lab notebooks into the lab. Backpacks, textbooks for other subjects, and other items should be stored elsewhere.

- Students should agree to never eat, drink, or smoke in any science laboratory. Food should **never** be brought into the laboratory

- Students should **never** taste or touch chemicals.

- Students should keep themselves and other objects away from Bunsen burner flames. Students should be responsible for checking, before they leave, that gas valves and hot plates are off.

- Students should know the proper fire drill procedures and the locations of fire exits.

- Students should always clean all apparatus and work areas.

- Students should wash their hands thoroughly with soap and water before leaving the lab room.

- Students should know the locations and operation of all safety equipment in the laboratory.

- Students should report all accidents or close calls to you immediately, no matter how minor.

- Students should **never** work alone in the laboratory, and they should never work unless you are present.

DISPOSAL OF CHEMICALS

Only a relatively small percentage of waste chemicals are classified as hazardous by EPA regulations. The EPA regulations are derived from two acts (as amended) passed by the Congress of the United States: RCRA (Resource Conservation and Recovery Act) and CERCLA (Comprehensive Environmental Response, Compensation, and Liability Act).

In addition, some states have enacted legislation governing the disposal of hazardous wastes that differs to some extent from the federal legislation. The disposal procedures described in this book have been designed to comply with the federal legislation as described in the EPA regulations.

In most cases the disposal procedures indicated in the teacher's edition will probably comply with your state's disposal requirements. However, to be sure of this, check with your state's environmental agency. If a particular disposal procedure does not comply with your state requirements, ask that agency to assist you in devising a procedure that is in compliance.

The following general practices are recommended in addition to the specific instructions given in the Lab Notes.

- Except when otherwise specified in the disposal procedures, neutralize acidic and basic wastes with 1.0 M potassium hydroxide, KOH, or 1.0 M sulfuric acid, H_2SO_4, added slowly and stirred.

- In dealing with a waste disposal contractor, prepare a complete list of the chemicals you want to dispose of. Classify each chemical on your disposal list as hazardous or nonhazardous waste. Check with your local environmental agency office for the details of such classification.

- Unlabeled bottles are a special problem. They must be identified to the extent that they can be classified as hazardous or nonhazardous waste. Some landfills will analyze a mystery bottle for a fee if it is shipped to the landfill in a separate package, is labeled as a sample, and includes instructions to analyze the contents sufficiently to allow proper disposal.

ELECTRIC SAFETY

Although none of the labs in this manual require electrical equipment, several include options for the use of microcomputer-based laboratory equipment, pH meters, or other equipment. The following safety precautions to avoid electrical shocks must be observed any time electrical equipment is present in the lab:

- Each electrical socket in the laboratory must be a three-hole socket and must be protected with a GFI (ground-fault interrupter) circuit.

- Check the polarity of all circuits with a polarity tester from an electronics supply store before you use them. Repair any incorrectly wired sockets.

- Use only electrical equipment that has a three-wire cord and three-prong plug.

- Be sure all electrical equipment is turned off before it is plugged into a socket. Turn off electrical equipment before you unplug it.

- Wiring hookups should be made or altered only when apparatus is disconnected from the power source and the power switch is turned off.

- Do not let electrical cords dangle from work stations; dangling cords are a shock hazard, and students can trip over them.
- Do not use electrical equipment with frayed or twisted cords.
- The area under and around electrical equipment should be dry; cords should not lie in puddles of spilled liquid.
- Your hands should be dry when you use electrical equipment.
- Do not use electrical equipment powered by 110–115 V alternating current for conductivity demonstrations or for any other use in which bare wires are exposed, even if the current is connected to a lower-voltage AC or DC connection.

Use dry cells or nicad rechargeable batteries as direct-current sources. Do not use automobile storage batteries or AC-to-DC converters; these two sources of DC current can present serious shock hazards.

Prepared by Jay A. Young, Consultant, Chemical Health and Safety, Silver Spring, Maryland

Incompatible Chemicals

Consider the following list when organizing and storing chemicals. Note that some chemicals on this list should no longer be in your lab, due to their potential risks. Consult your state and local guidelines for more specific information on chemical hazard.

Chemical	Should not come in contact with
acetic acid	chromic acid, nitric acid, perchloric acid, ethylene glycol, hydroxyl compounds, peroxides, or permanganates
acetone	concentrated sulfuric acid or nitric acid mixtures
acetylene	silver, mercury, or their compounds; bromine, chlorine, fluorine, or copper tubing
alkali metals, powdered aluminum or magnesium	water, carbon dioxide, carbon tetrachloride, or the halogens
ammonia (anhydrous)	mercury, hydrogen fluoride, or calcium hypochlorite
ammonium nitrate (strong oxidizer)	strong acids, metal powders, chlorates, sulfur, flammable liquids, or finely divided organic materials
aniline	nitric acid or hydrogen peroxide
bromine	ammonia, acetylene, butane, hydrogen, sodium carbide, turpentine, or finely divided metals
carbon (activated)	calcium hypochlorite or any oxidizing agent
chlorates	ammonium salts, strong acids, powdered metals, sulfur, or finely divided organic materials
chromic acid	glacial acetic acid, camphor, glycerin, naphthalene, turpentine, low-molar-mass alcohols, or flammable liquids
chlorine	same as bromine
copper	acetylene or hydrogen peroxide
flammable liquids	ammonium nitrate, chromic acid, hydrogen peroxide, sodium peroxide, nitric acid, or any of the halogens
hydrocarbons (butane, propane, gasoline, turpentine)	fluorine, chlorine, bromine, chromic acid, or sodium peroxide
hydrofluoric acid	ammonia
hydrogen peroxide	most metals or their salts, flammable liquids, or other combustible materials
hydrogen sulfide	nitric acid or certain other oxidizing gases
iodine	acetylene or ammonia
nitric acid	glacial acetic acid, chromic or hydrocyanic acids, hydrogen sulfide, flammable liquids, or flammable gases that are easily nitrated

Chemical	Should not come in contact with
oxygen	oils, grease, hydrogen, or flammable substances
perchloric acid	acetic anhydride, bismuth or its alloys, alcohols, paper, wood, or other organic materials
phosphorus pentoxide	water
potassium permanganate	glycerin, ethylene glycol, or sulfuric acid
silver	acetylene, ammonium compounds, oxalic acid, or tartaric acid
sodium peroxide	glacial acetic acid, acetic anhydride, methanol, carbon disulfide, glycerin, benzaldehyde, or water
sulfuric acid	chlorates, perchlorates, permanganates, or water

Introduction to the Lab Program

Structure of the Experiments

INTRODUCTION

The opening paragraphs set the theme for the experiment and summarize its major concepts.

OBJECTIVES

Objectives highlight the key concepts to be learned in the experiment and emphasize the science process skills and techniques of scientific inquiry.

MATERIALS

These lists enable you to organize all apparatus and materials needed to perform the experiment. Knowing the concentrations of solutions is vital. You often need this information to perform calculations and to answer the questions at the end of the experiment.

SAFETY

Safety cautions are placed at the beginning of the experiment to alert you to procedures that may require special care. Before you begin, you should review the safety issues that apply to the experiment.

PROCEDURE

By following the procedures of an experiment, you perform concrete laboratory operations that duplicate the fact-gathering techniques used by professional chemists. You learn skills in the laboratory. The procedures tell you how and where to record observations and data.

DATA AND CALCULATIONS TABLES

The data that you collect during each experiment should be recorded in the labeled Data Tables provided. The entries you make in a Calculations Table emphasize the mathematical, physical, and chemical relationships that exist among the accumulated data. Both types of tables should help you to think logically and to formulate your conclusions about what occurs during the experiment.

CALCULATIONS

Space is provided for all computations based on the data you gather.

QUESTIONS

Based on the data and calculations, you should be able to develop plausible explanations for the phenomena you observe during the experiment. Specific questions require you to draw on the concepts you learn.

GENERAL CONCLUSIONS

This section asks broader questions that bring together the results and conclusions of the experiment and relate them to other situations.

Safety in the Chemistry Laboratory

CHEMICALS ARE NOT TOYS.

Any chemical can be dangerous if it is misused. Always follow the instructions for the experiment. Pay close attention to the safety notes. Do not do anything differently unless told to do so by your teacher.

Chemicals, even water, can cause harm. The trick is to know how to use chemicals correctly so that they will not cause harm. You can do this by following the rules on these pages, paying attention to your teacher's directions, and following the cautions on chemical labels and experiments.

These safety rules always apply in the lab.

1. Always wear a lab apron and safety goggles.

Even if you aren't working on an experiment, laboratories contain chemicals that can damage your clothing, so wear your apron and keep the strings of the apron tied. Because chemicals can cause eye damage, even blindness, you must wear safety goggles. If your safety goggles are uncomfortable or get clouded up, ask your teacher for help. Try lengthening the strap a bit, washing the goggles with soap and warm water, or using an antifog spray.

2. Generally, no contact lenses are allowed in the lab.

Even while wearing safety goggles, you can get chemicals between contact lenses and your eyes, and they can cause irreparable eye damage. If your doctor requires that you wear contact lenses instead of glasses, then you may need to wear special safety goggles in the lab. Ask your doctor or your teacher about them.

3. Never work alone in the laboratory.

You should always do lab work under the supervision of your teacher.

4. Wear the right clothing for lab work.

Necklaces, neckties, dangling jewelry, long hair, and loose clothing can cause you to knock things over or catch items on fire. Tuck in a necktie or take it off. Do not wear a necklace or other dangling jewelry, including hanging earrings. It isn't necessary, but it might be a good idea to remove your wristwatch so that it is not damaged by a chemical splash.

Pull back long hair, and tie it in place. Nylon and polyester fabrics burn and melt more readily than cotton, so wear cotton clothing if you can. It's best to wear fitted garments, but if your clothing is loose or baggy, tuck it in or tie it back so that it does not get in the way or catch on fire.

Wear shoes that will protect your feet from chemical spills—no open-toed shoes, sandals, or shoes made of woven leather straps. Shoes made of solid leather or a polymer are much better than shoes made of cloth. Also, wear pants, not shorts or skirts.

5. Only books and notebooks needed for the experiment should be in the lab.

Do not bring other textbooks, purses, bookbags, backpacks, or other items into the lab; keep these things in your desk or locker.

6. Read the entire experiment before entering the lab.
Memorize the safety precautions. Be familiar with the instructions for the experiment. Only materials and equipment authorized by your teacher should be used. When you do the lab work, follow the instructions and the safety precautions described in the directions for the experiment.

7. Read chemical labels.
Follow the instructions and safety precautions stated on the labels. Know the location of Material Safety Data Sheets for chemicals.

8. Walk carefully in the lab.
Sometimes you will carry chemicals from the supply station to your lab station. Avoid bumping other students and spilling the chemicals. Stay at your lab station at other times.

9. Food, beverages, chewing gum, cosmetics, and tobacco are *never* allowed in the lab.
You already know this.

10. Never taste chemicals or touch them with your bare hands.
Also, keep your hands away from your face and mouth while working, even if you are wearing gloves.

11. Use a sparker to light a Bunsen burner.
Do not use matches. Be sure that all gas valves are turned off and that all hot plates are turned off and unplugged before you leave the lab.

12. Be careful with hot plates, Bunsen burners, and other heat sources.
Keep your body and clothing away from flames. Do not touch a hot plate just after it has been turned off. It is probably hotter than you think. Use tongs to heat glassware, crucibles, and other things and to remove them from a hot plate, a drying oven, or the flame of a Bunsen burner.

13. Do not use electrical equipment with frayed or twisted cords or wires.

14. Be sure your hands are dry before you use electrical equipment.
Before plugging an electrical cord into a socket, be sure the electrical equipment is turned off. When you are finished with it, turn it off. Before you leave the lab, unplug it, but be sure to turn it off first.

15. Do not let electrical cords dangle from work stations; dangling cords can cause tripping or electric shocks.
The area under and around electrical equipment should be dry; cords should not lie in puddles of spilled liquid.

16. Know fire drill procedures and the locations of exits.

17. Know the locations and operation of safety showers and eyewash stations.

18. If your clothes catch on fire, *walk* to the safety shower, stand under it, and turn it on.

19. **If you get a chemical in your eyes, walk immediately to the eyewash station, turn it on, and lower your head so that your eyes are in the running water.**

   Hold your eyelids open with your thumbs and fingers, and roll your eyeballs around. You have to flush your eyes continuously for at least 15 min. Call your teacher while you are doing this.

20. **If you have a spill on the floor or lab bench, don't try to clean it up by yourself.**

   First, ask your teacher if it is OK for you to do the cleanup; if it is not, your teacher will know how the spill should be cleaned up safely.

21. **If you spill a chemical on your skin, wash it off under the sink faucet, and call your teacher.**

   If you spill a solid chemical on your clothing, brush it off carefully so that you do not scatter it, and call your teacher. If you get a liquid chemical on your clothing, wash it off right away if you can get it under the sink faucet, and call your teacher. If the spill is on clothing that will not fit under the sink faucet, use the safety shower. Remove the affected clothing while under the shower, and call your teacher. (It may be temporarily embarrassing to remove your clothing in front of your class, but failing to flush that chemical off your skin could cause permanent damage.)

22. **The best way to prevent an accident is to stop it before it happens.**

   If you have a close call, tell your teacher so that you and your teacher can find a way to prevent it from happening again. Otherwise, the next time, it could be a harmful accident instead of just a close call.

23. **All accidents should be reported to your teacher, no matter how minor.**

   Also, if you get a headache, feel sick to your stomach, or feel dizzy, tell your teacher immediately.

24. **For all chemicals, take only what you need.**

   On the other hand, if you do happen to take too much and have some left over, **do not** put it back in the bottle. If somebody accidentally puts a chemical into the wrong bottle, the next person to use it will have a contaminated sample. Ask your teacher what to do with any leftover chemicals.

25. *Never* **take any chemicals out of the lab.**

   You should already know this rule.

26. **Horseplay and fooling around in the lab are very dangerous.**

   Never be a clown in the laboratory.

27. **Keep your work area clean and tidy.**

   After your work is done, clean your work area and all equipment.

28. **Always wash your hands with soap and water before you leave the lab.**

29. **Whether or not the lab instructions remind you, *all* of these rules *apply all of the time.***

QUIZ

Determine which safety rules apply to the following.

• Tie back long hair, and confine loose clothing. (Rule ? applies.)

• Never reach across an open flame. (Rule ? applies.)

• Use proper procedures when lighting Bunsen burners. Turn off hot plates and Bunsen burners that are not in use. (Rule ? applies.)

• Be familiar with the procedures and know the safety precautions before you begin. (Rule ? applies.)

• Use tongs when heating containers. Never hold or touch containers with your hands while heating them. Always allow heated materials to cool before handling them. (Rule ? applies.)

• Turn off gas valves that are not in use. (Rule ? applies.)

SAFETY SYMBOLS

To highlight specific types of precautions, the following symbols are used in the experiments. Remember that no matter what safety symbols and instructions appear in each experiment, all of the 29 safety rules described previously should be followed at all times.

EYE AND CLOTHING PROTECTION

• Wear safety goggles in the laboratory at all times. Know how to use the eyewash station.

• Wear laboratory aprons in the laboratory. Keep the apron strings tied so that they do not dangle.

CHEMICAL SAFETY

• Never taste, eat, or swallow any chemicals in the laboratory. Do not eat or drink any food from laboratory containers. Beakers are not cups, and evaporating dishes are not bowls.

• Never return unused chemicals to their original containers.

• Some chemicals are harmful to the environment. You can help protect the environment by following the instructions for proper disposal.

• It helps to label the beakers and test tubes containing chemicals.

• Never transfer substances by sucking on a pipet or straw; use a suction bulb.

• Never place glassware, containers of chemicals, or anything else near the edges of a lab bench or table.

CAUSTIC SUBSTANCES

• If a chemical gets on your skin or clothing or in your eyes, rinse it immediately, and alert your teacher.

• If a chemical is spilled on the floor or lab bench, tell your teacher, but do not clean it up yourself unless your teacher says it is OK to do so.

HEATING SAFETY

- When heating a chemical in a test tube, always point the open end of the test tube away from yourself and other people.

EXPLOSION PRECAUTION

- Use flammable liquids in small amounts only.
- When working with flammable liquids, be sure that no one else in the lab is using a lit Bunsen burner or plans to use one. Make sure there are no other heat sources present.

HAND SAFETY

- Always wear gloves or use cloths to protect your hands when cutting, fire polishing, or bending hot glass tubing. Keep cloths clear of any flames.
- Never force glass tubing into rubber tubing, rubber stoppers, or corks. To protect your hands, wear heavy leather gloves or wrap toweling around the glass and the tubing, stopper, or cork, and gently push the glass tubing into the rubber or cork.
- Use tongs when heating test tubes. Never hold a test tube in your hand to heat it.
- Always allow hot glassware to cool before you handle it.

GLASSWARE SAFETY

- Check the condition of glassware before and after using it. Inform your teacher of any broken, chipped, or cracked glassware because it should not be used.
- Do not pick up broken glass with your bare hands. Place broken glass in a specially designated disposal container.

GAS PRECAUTION

- Do not inhale fumes directly. When instructed to smell a substance, waft it toward you. That is, use your hand to wave the fumes toward your nose. Inhale gently.

RADIATION PRECAUTION

- Always wear gloves when handling a radioactive source.
- Always wear safety goggles when performing experiments with radioactive materials.
- Always wash your hands and arms thoroughly after working with radioactive materials.

HYGIENIC CARE

- Keep your hands away from your face and mouth.
- Always wash your hands before leaving the laboratory.

Any time you see any of the safety symbols, you should remember that all 29 of the numbered laboratory rules always apply.

Labeling of Chemicals

In any science laboratory the labeling of chemical containers, reagent bottles, and equipment is essential for safe operations. Proper labeling can lower the potential for accidents that occur as a result of misuse. Read labels and equipment instructions several times before you use chemicals or equipment. Be sure that you are using the correct items, that you know how to use them, and that you are aware of any hazards or precautions associated with their use.

All chemical containers and reagent bottles should be labeled prominently and accurately with labeling materials that are not affected by chemicals.

Chemical labels should contain the following information:

1. **Name of the chemical and its chemical formula**

2. **Statement of possible hazards** This is indicated by the use of an appropriate signal word, such as *DANGER*, *WARNING*, or *CAUTION*. This signal word usually is accompanied by a word that indicates the type of hazard present, such as *POISON*, *CAUSES BURNS*, *EXPLOSIVE*, or *FLAMMABLE*. Note that this labeling should not take the place of reading the appropriate Material Safety Data Sheet for a chemical.

3. **Precautionary measures** Precautionary measures describe how users can avoid injury from the hazards listed on the label. Examples include: "use only with adequate ventilation" and "do not get in eyes or on skin or clothing."

4. **Instructions in case of contact or exposure** If accidental contact or exposure does occur, immediate first-aid measures can minimize injury. For example, the label on a bottle of acid should include this instruction: "In case of contact, flush with large amounts of water; for eyes, rinse freely with water for 15 min and get medical attention immediately."

5. **The date of preparation and the name of the person who prepared the chemical** This information is important for maintaining a safe chemical inventory.

Suggested Labeling Scheme	
Name of contents	hydrochloric acid
Chemical formula and concentration or physical state	6 M HCl
Statements of possible hazards and precautionary and measures	WARNING! CAUSTIC and CORROSIVE—CAUSES BURNS Avoid contact with skin and eyes Avoid breathing vapors.
Hazard Instructions for contact or overexposure	IN CASE OF CONTACT: Immediately flush skin or eyes with large amounts of water for at least 15 min; for eyes, get medical attention immediately!
Date prepared or obtained Manufacturer (commercially obtained) or preparer (locally made)	May 8, 2005 Prepared by Betsy Byron, Faribault High School, Faribault, Minnesota

Laboratory Techniques

Figure A   **Figure B**   **Figure C**

DECANTING AND TRANSFERRING LIQUIDS

1. The safest way to transfer a liquid from a graduated cylinder to a test tube is shown in **Figure A.** Transfer the liquid at arm's length with your elbows slightly bent. This position enables you to see what you are doing and still maintain steady control.

2. Sometimes liquids contain particles of insoluble solids that sink to the bottom of a test tube or beaker. Use one of the methods given below to separate a supernatant (the clear fluid) from insoluble solids.

   a. Figure B shows the proper method of decanting a supernatant liquid in a test tube.

   b. Figure C shows the proper method of decanting a supernatant liquid in a beaker by using a stirring rod. The rod should touch the wall of the receiving container. Hold the stirring rod against the lip of the beaker containing the supernatant liquid. As you pour, the liquid will run down the rod and fall into the beaker resting below. Using this method will prevent the liquid from running down the side of the beaker you are pouring from.

HEATING SUBSTANCES AND EVAPORATING SOLUTIONS

1. Use care in selecting glassware for high-temperature heating. The glassware should be heat resistant.

2. When using a gas flame to heat glassware, use a ceramic-centered wire gauze to protect glassware from direct contact with the flame. Wire gauzes can withstand extremely high temperatures and will help prevent glassware from breaking. **Figure D** shows the proper setup for evaporating a solution over a water bath.

Watch glass with solution

Beaker

Boiling water

Wire gauze (ceramic centered)

Figure D

Figure E

Figure F

3. In some experiments you are required to heat a substance to high temperatures in a porcelain crucible. **Figure E** shows the proper apparatus setup used to accomplish this task.

4. Figure F shows the proper setup for evaporating a solution in a porcelain evaporating dish with a watch glass cover that prevents spattering.

5. Glassware, porcelain, and iron rings that have been heated may look cool after they are removed from a heat source, but they can burn your skin even after several minutes of cooling. Use tongs, test tube holders, or heat-resistant mitts and pads whenever you handle this apparatus.

6. You can test the temperature of questionable beakers, ring stands, wire gauzes, or other pieces of apparatus that have been heated, by holding the back of your hand close to their surfaces before grasping them. You will be able to feel any heat generated from the hot surfaces. **Do not touch the apparatus until it is cool.**

POURING LIQUID FROM A REAGENT BOTTLE

1. Read the label at least three times before using the contents of a reagent bottle.

2. Never lay the stopper of a reagent bottle on the lab table.

3. When pouring a caustic or corrosive liquid into a beaker, use a stirring rod to avoid drips and spills. Hold the stirring rod against the lip of the reagent bottle. Estimate the amount of liquid you need, and pour this amount along the rod into the beaker. See **Figure G**.

Figure G

4. Take extra precautions when handling a bottle of acid or strong base. Remember the following important rules: Never add water to any concentrated acid, particularly sulfuric acid, because the mixture can splash and will generate a lot of heat. To dilute any acid, add the acid to water in small quantities, while stirring slowly. Remember the "triple A's"—Always Add Acid to water.

5. Examine the outside of the reagent bottle for any liquid that has dripped down the bottle or spilled on the counter top. Your teacher will show you the proper procedures for cleaning up a chemical spill.

6. Never pour reagents back into stock bottles. At the end of the experiment, your teacher will tell you how to dispose of any excess chemicals.

HEATING MATERIAL IN A TEST TUBE

1. Check to see that the test tube is heat resistant.

2. Always use a test-tube holder or clamp when heating a test tube.

3. Never point a heated test tube at anyone, because the liquid may splash out of the test tube.

4. Never look down into the test tube while heating it.

5. Heat the test tube from the upper portions of the tube downward and continuously move the test tube, as indicated in **Figure H.** Do not heat any one spot on the test tube. Otherwise, a pressure buildup may cause the bottom of the tube to blow out.

USING A MORTAR AND PESTLE

1. A mortar and pestle should be used for grinding only one substance at a time. See **Figure I.**

2. Never use a mortar and pestle for simultaneously mixing different substances.

3. Place the substance to be broken up into the mortar.

4. Firmly push on the pestle to crush the substance. Then grind it to pulverize it.

5. Remove the powdered substance with a porcelain spoon.

Figure H   **Figure I**   **Figure J**

DETECTING ODORS SAFELY

1. Test for the odor of gases by wafting your hand over the test tube and cautiously sniffing the fumes, as indicated in **Figure J.**

2. Do not inhale any fumes directly.

3. Use a fume hood whenever poisonous or irritating fumes are involved. **Do not waft and sniff poisonous or irritating fumes.**

Laboratory Procedures

Teacher Notes

TIME REQUIRED Two 45-minute lab periods

SKILLS ACQUIRED

Collecting data
Experimenting
Identifying patterns
Interpreting
Measuring
Organizing and analyzing data

RATING

Easy ◄——¹——²——³——⁴——► Hard

Teacher Prep–2
Student Set-Up–2
Concept Level–1
Clean Up–2

THE SCIENTIFIC METHOD

Make Observations Students make various types of measurements and collect these data.

Analyze the Results Students will analyze the results of this lab in analysis questions 6, 7, 8, 10, and 12.

Draw Conclusions Students will draw conclusions through the questions in the Safety Check section.

Communicate the Results Students will communicate their results through analysis questions 2, 3, 4, 5, 9, 11, and 13.

MATERIALS

Materials for this lab activity can be purchased from Sergent-Welch. See the Lab Materials QuickList software on the **One-Stop Planner** CD-ROM for ordering instructions.

SAFETY CAUTIONS

Discuss all safety symbols and caution statements with students.

Loose hair and clothing must be tied back.

If students find a gas valve that has not been turned off properly, the room must be thoroughly ventilated, using the hood and windows in order to prevent a fire hazard.

Remind students of the following safety precautions:

• Always wear safety goggles, gloves, and a lab apron to protect your eyes and clothing. If you get a chemical in your eyes, immediately flush the chemical out at the eyewash station while calling to your teacher. Know the location of the emergency lab shower and the eyewash stations and procedures for using them.

Laboratory Procedures *continued*

- Do not touch any chemicals. If you get a chemical on your skin or clothing, wash the chemical off at the sink while calling to your teacher. Make sure you carefully read the labels and follow the precautions on all containers of chemicals that you use. If there are no precautions stated on the label, ask your teacher what precautions you should follow. Do not taste any chemicals or items used in the laboratory. Never return leftover chemicals to their original containers; take only small amounts to avoid wasting supplies.

- When using a Bunsen burner, confine long hair and loose clothing. If your clothing catches on fire, WALK to the emergency lab shower, and use it to put out the fire. Do not heat glassware that is broken, chipped, or cracked. Use tongs or a hot mitt to handle heated glassware and other equipment because heated glassware does not look hot.

- When you insert glass tubing into stoppers, lubricate the glass with water or glycerin and protect your hands and fingers: Wear leather gloves or place folded cloth pads between both of your hands and the glass tubing. Then *gently* push the tubing into the stopper hole. In the same way, protect your hands and fingers when removing glass tubing from stoppers and from rubber or plastic tubing.

- Call your teacher in the event of a spill. Spills should be cleaned up promptly, according to your teacher's directions.

- Never put broken glass in a regular waste container. Broken glass should be disposed of properly.

DISPOSAL

There are no special disposal guidelines. The sodium chloride can be reused by each class if you designate a special container for NaCl disposal after each part. Keep this NaCl separate from the NaCl you use as a reagent. The same is true for the copper wire and the sand.

TECHNIQUES TO DEMONSTRATE

Show the students the proper method for filling a buret. Strongly caution students against reaching above their head to fill a buret.

Demonstrate the proper method of fire polishing glass tubing.

Show students how to read a meniscus.

Show students how to properly place filter paper in a funnel.

Demonstrate how to pour liquid from a beaker using a glass stirring rod.

Review proper safety precautions required when dealing with chemicals.

Show the students the proper method for filling and using a pipet.

Review proper disposal and clean up procedures with students.

TIPS AND TRICKS

Although all the techniques are carefully described, there is no substitute for seeing each of them demonstrated before students try them themselves.

Close supervision is necessary if students work with glass tubing. Emphasize that they should never attempt to force tubing into stoppers with excessive force. Advise them to use a lubricant such as water or glycerin to help ease the tubing in.

Stress to students that hot tubing or other glassware does not look hot, and care should be taken to avoid burns.

Advise students to read and follow the procedures carefully.

Name _____ Class _____ Date _____

Laboratory Procedures

The best way to become familiar with chemical apparatus is to handle the pieces yourself in the laboratory. This experiment is divided into several parts in which you will learn how to adjust the gas burner, insert glass tubing into a rubber stopper, use a balance, handle solids, measure liquids, and filter a mixture. Great emphasis is placed on safety precautions that should be observed whenever you perform an experiment and use the apparatus. In many of the later experiments, references will be made to these "Laboratory Techniques." In later experiments you will also be referred to the safety precautions and procedures explained in all parts of this experiment. It is important that you develop a positive approach to a safe and healthful environment in the lab.

OBJECTIVES

Observe proper safety techniques with all laboratory equipment.

Use laboratory apparatus skillfully and efficiently.

Recognize the names and functions of all apparatus in the laboratory.

Develop a positive approach toward laboratory safety.

 Always wear safety goggles, gloves, and a lab apron to protect your eyes and clothing. If you get a chemical in your eyes, immediately flush the chemical out at the eyewash station while calling to your teacher. Know the location of the emergency lab shower and eyewash station and the procedures for using them.

Do not touch any chemicals. If you get a chemical on your skin or clothing, wash the chemical off at the sink while calling to your teacher. Make sure you carefully read the labels and follow the precautions on all containers of chemicals that you use. If there are no precautions stated on the label, ask your teacher what precautions to follow. Do not taste any chemicals or items used in the laboratory. Never return leftover chemicals to their original containers; take only small amounts to avoid wasting supplies.

Do not heat glassware that is broken, chipped, or cracked. Use tongs or a hot mitt to handle heated glassware and other equipment because hot glassware does not always look hot.

When using a Bunsen burner, confine long hair and loose clothing. If your clothing catches on fire, WALK to the emergency lab shower and use it to put out the fire.

When heating a substance in a test tube, the mouth of the test tube should point away from where you and others are standing. Watch the test tube at all times to prevent the contents from boiling over.

Name _____ Class _____ Date _____

Laboratory Procedures *continued*

 Never put broken glass in a regular waste container. Broken glass should be disposed of separately according to your teacher's instructions.

When you insert glass tubing into stoppers, lubricate the glass with water or glycerin and protect your hands and fingers. Wear leather gloves or place folded cloth pads between both your hands and the glass tubing. Then *gently* push the tubing into the stopper hole. In the same way, protect your hands and fingers when removing glass tubing from stoppers and from rubber or plastic tubing.

PART 1—THE BURNER

MATERIALS

- Bunsen burner and related equipment
- copper wire, 18 gauge
- evaporating dish
- forceps
- heat-resistant gloves

- heat-resistant mat
- lab apron
- safety goggles
- sparker

Procedure

1. Put on safety goggles, and a lab apron. Use heat-resistant gloves when handling hot items.

2. The Bunsen burner is commonly used as a source of heat in the laboratory. Look at **Figure 1** as you examine your Bunsen burner and identify the parts. Although the details of construction vary among burners, each has a gas inlet located in the base, a vertical tube or barrel in which the gas is mixed with air, and adjustable openings or ports in the base of the barrel. These ports admit air to the gas stream. The burner may have an adjustable needle valve to regulate the flow of gas. In some models the gas flow is regulated simply by adjusting the gas valve on the supply line. The burner is always turned off at the gas valve, never at the needle valve.

   CAUTION: Before you light the burner, check to see that you and your partner have taken the following safety precautions against fires: Wear safety goggles, aprons, and heat-resistant gloves. Confine long hair and loose clothing: tie long hair at the back of the head and away from the front of the face, and roll up long sleeves on shirts, blouses, and sweaters away from the wrists. You should also know the locations of fire extinguishers, fire blankets, safety showers, and sand buckets and the procedure for using them in case of a fire.

Laboratory Procedures *continued*

Figure 1

Labels on figure: a, b, c, Barrel, Air ports, Air enters here, Base, Needle valve, Gas enters here, Burner tubing, Gas valve, Gas line

3. When lighting the burner, partially close the ports at the base of the barrel, turn the gas full on, hold the sparker about 5 cm above the top of the burner, and proceed to light. The gas flow may then be regulated by adjusting the gas valve until the flame has the desired height. If a very low flame is needed, remember that the ports should be partially closed when the gas pressure is reduced. Otherwise the flame may burn inside the base of the barrel. When the flame is improperly burning in this way, the barrel will get very hot, and the flame will produce a poisonous gas, carbon monoxide.

CAUTION: If the flame is burning inside the base of the barrel, immediately turn off the gas at the gas valve. Do not touch the barrel, because it is extremely hot. Allow the barrel of the burner to cool, and then proceed as follows:

Begin again, but first decrease the amount of air admitted to the burner by partially closing the ports. Turn the gas full on, and then relight the burner. Control the height of the flame by adjusting the gas valve. By taking these steps, you should acquire a flame that is burning safely and is easily regulated.

4. Once you have a flame that is burning safely and steadily, you can experiment by completely closing the ports at the base of the burner. What effect does this have on the flame?

When the ports at the base are closed, a yellow flame results.

_____

_____

Laboratory Procedures *continued*

Using the forceps, hold an evaporating dish in the tip of the flame for about 3 min. Place the dish on a heat-resistant mat and allow the dish to cool. Then examine the bottom of the dish. Describe the results and suggest a possible explanation.

The yellow flame leaves a black deposit on the bottom of the evaporating

dish. The lack of air to the burner results in incomplete combustion, the

luminous flame, and the deposit of soot.

Such a flame is seldom used in the lab. For laboratory work, you should adjust the burner so that the flame is free of yellow color, nonluminous, and also free of the roaring sound caused by admitting too much air.

5. Regulate the flow of gas so that the flame extends roughly 8 cm above the barrel. Now adjust the supply of air until you have a noisy, steady flame with a sharply defined, light-blue inner cone. This adjustment gives the highest temperature possible with your burner. Using the forceps, insert a 10-cm piece of copper wire into the flame just above the barrel. Lift the wire slowly up through parts of the flame. Where is the hottest portion of the flame located?

The hottest portion of the nonluminous flame is just above the tip of the

light blue cone b.

Hold the wire in this part of the flame for a few seconds. What happens?

The copper wire becomes red hot and begins to soften (melt).

6. Shut off the gas burner. Now think about what you have just observed in steps **4** and **5**. Why is the nonluminous flame preferred over the yellow luminous flame in the laboratory?

The nonluminous flame burns cleaner than the yellow flame.

7. Clean the evaporating dish and put away the burner. All the equipment you store in the lab locker or drawer should be completely cool, clean, and dry. Be sure that the valve on the gas jet is completely shut off. Remember to wash your hands thoroughly with soap at the end of each laboratory period.

PART 2—GLASS MANIPULATION

MATERIALS

- cloth pads or leather gloves
- glass funnel
- lab apron
- rubber hose
- rubber stopper, 1-hole
- safety goggles
- water or glycerin

Procedure

1. Inserting glass tubing into rubber stoppers can be very dangerous. The following precautions should be observed to prevent injuries:

   a. Never attempt to insert glass tubing that has a jagged end. Glass tubing should be fire polished before it is inserted into a rubber stopper. To fire polish glass tubing, heat the end in a flame until the end is smooth. **Never fire polish anything without your teacher's permission, and proper supervision. Use tongs or a hot mitt to handle heated glassware and other equipment, because heated glassware does not look hot.**

   b. Use water or glycerin as a lubricant on the end of the glass tubing before inserting it into a rubber stopper. Ask your teacher for the proper lubricant. **CAUTION: Protect your hands and fingers when inserting glass tubing into a rubber stopper.**

   c. Wear leather gloves or place folded cloth pads between your hands and the glass tubing. Hold the glass tubing as close as possible to the part where it is to enter the rubber stopper. Always point the glass tubing away from the palm of your hand that holds the stopper, as shown in **Figure 2** below. Using a twisting motion, gently push the tubing into the stopper hole.

   Figure 2

   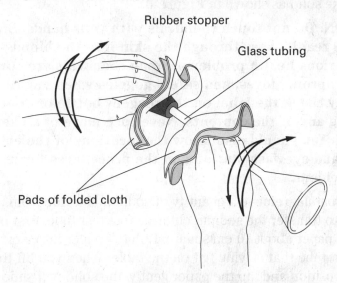

   Rubber stopper

   Glass tubing

   Pads of folded cloth

   d. At the end of the experiment, put on leather gloves, or place folded cloth pads between your hands and the glass tubing, and remove the rubber stoppers from the tubing to keep them from sticking or "freezing" to the glass. Use a lubricant, as directed in **step 1b**, if the stopper or tubing won't budge.

2. When inserting glass tubing into a rubber or plastic hose, observe the same precautions discussed in **steps 1a–1c.** The glass tubing should be lubricated before inserting it into the rubber or plastic hose. The rubber hose should be cut at an angle before the insertion of the glass tubing. The angled cut in the hose allows the rubber to stretch more readily.

CAUTION: Protect your hands when inserting or removing glass tubing.

At the end of an experiment, immediately remove the glass tubing from the hose. When disassembling, follow the precautions that were given in **step 1d.**

Carefully follow these precautions and techniques whenever an experiment requires that you insert glass tubing into either a rubber stopper or a rubber or plastic hose. You will be referred to these safety precautions, wherever appropriate, throughout the lab course.

PART 3—HANDLING SOLIDS

MATERIALS

- glazed paper
- gloves
- lab apron
- safety goggles

- sodium chloride
- spatula
- test tube

Procedure

1. Solids are usually kept in wide-mouthed bottles. A spatula should be used to dip out the solid as shown in **Figure 3.**

   CAUTION: Do not touch chemicals with your hands. Some chemical reagents readily pass through the skin into the bloodstream and can cause serious health problems. Some chemicals are corrosive. Always wear an apron, gloves, and safety goggles when handling chemicals. Carefully check the label on the reagent bottle or container before removing any of the contents. Never use more of a chemical than directed. You should also know the locations of the emergency lab shower and eyewash station and the procedures for using them in case of an accident.

   Using a spatula, remove a quantity of sodium chloride from its reagent bottle. In order to transfer the sodium chloride to a test tube, first place it on a piece of glazed paper about 10 cm square. Roll the paper into a cylinder and slide it into a test tube that is lying flat on the table. When you lift the tube to a vertical position and tap the paper gently, the solid will slide down into the test tube, as shown in **Figure 4.**

   CAUTION: Never try to pour a solid from a bottle into a test tube. As a precaution against contamination, never pour unused chemicals back into their reagent bottles.

2. Dispose of the solid sodium chloride and the glazed paper in the waste jars or containers provided by your teacher.

   CAUTION: Never discard chemicals or broken glassware in the waste paper basket. This is an important safety precaution against fires, and it prevents personal injuries (such as hand cuts) to anyone who empties the wastepaper basket.

3. Remember to clean up the lab station and to wash your hands at the end of this part of the experiment.

Figure 3	**Figure 4**

Spatula

PART 4—THE BALANCE

MATERIALS

- balance, centigram
- glazed paper
- gloves
- lab apron
- safety goggles
- sodium chloride
- spatula
- weighing paper

Procedure

1. When a balance is required for determining mass, you will use a centigram balance like the one shown in **Figure 5.** The centigram balance has a readability of 0.01 g. This means that your mass readings should all be recorded to the nearest 0.01 g.

2. Before using the balance, always check to see if the pointer is resting at zero. If the pointer is not at zero, check the riders on the scales. If all the scale riders are at zero, turn the zero-adjust knob until the pointer rests at zero. The zero-adjust knob is usually located at the far left end of the balance beam, as shown in **Figure 5.** Note: The balance will not adjust to zero if the movable pan has been removed. **Never place chemicals or hot objects directly on the balance pan.** Always use weighing paper or a glass container. Chemicals can permanently damage the surface of the balance pan and affect the accuracy of measurements.

Name _____ Class _____ Date _____

Laboratory Procedures *continued*

Figure 5

3. In many experiments, you will be asked to determine the mass of a specified amount of a chemical solid. Use the following procedure to obtain approximately 13 g of sodium chloride.

   a. Make sure that the pointer on the balance is set at zero. Obtain a piece of weighing paper and place it on the balance pan. Determine the mass of the paper by adjusting the riders on the various scales. Record the mass of the weighing paper to the nearest 0.01 g.

   Mass of paper: Student Answer

   b. Add 13 grams to the balance by sliding the rider on the 100 g scale to 10 and the rider on the 10 g scale to 3.

   c. Using a spatula, obtain a quantity of sodium chloride from the reagent bottle and place it on a separate piece of glazed paper.

   d. Now slowly pour the sodium chloride from the glazed paper onto the weighing paper on the balance pan until the pointer once again comes to zero. In most cases, you will only have to be close to the specified mass. Do not waste time trying to obtain exactly 13.00 g. Instead, read the exact mass when the pointer rests close to zero and you have around 13 g of sodium chloride in the balance pan. The mass might be 13.18 g. Record your exact mass of sodium chloride and the weighing paper to the nearest 0.01 g. (Hint: Remember to subtract the mass of the weighing paper to find the mass of sodium chloride.)

   Mass of NaCl and paper: Student Answer

4. Wash your hands thoroughly with soap and water at the end of each lab period.

Laboratory Procedures *continued*

PART 5—MEASURING LIQUIDS

MATERIALS

- beaker, 50 mL
- beaker, 250 mL
- buret
- buret clamp
- gloves
- graduated cylinder, 100 mL
- lab apron
- pipet
- ring stand
- safety goggles
- water

Procedure

1. For approximate measurements of liquids, a graduated cylinder, such as the one shown in **Figure 6,** is generally used. These cylinders are usually graduated in milliliters (mL), reading from the bottom up. They may also have a second column of graduations reading from top to bottom. Examine your cylinder for these markings. Record the capacity and describe the scale of your cylinder in the space below.

   Observations: <u>Student Answers</u>

   _____

Figure 6

Figure 7

2. A pipet or a buret is used for more accurate volume measurements. Pipets, which are made in many sizes, are used to deliver measured volumes of liquids. A pipet is fitted with a suction bulb, as shown in **Figure 7.** The bulb is used to withdraw air from the pipet while drawing up the liquid to be measured.

   CAUTION: Always use the suction bulb. NEVER pipet by mouth.

Name _____ Class _____ Date _____

| Laboratory Procedures *continued*

3. Burets are used for delivering any desired quantity of liquid up to the capacity of the buret. Many burets are graduated in tenths of milliliters. When using a buret, follow these steps:

a. Clamp the buret in position on a ring stand, as shown in **Figure 8.**

b. Place a 250-mL beaker under the tip of the buret. The beaker serves to catch any liquid that is released.

c. Pour a quantity of liquid that you want to measure from the liquid's reagent bottle into a 50-mL beaker. (NOTE: In this first trial, you will use water.) Pour the liquid from the beaker into the top of the buret, being careful to avoid spills. (NOTE: Always carefully check the label of any reagent bottle before removing any liquid).

CAUTION: Never pour a liquid directly from its reagent bottle into the buret. You should first pour the liquid into a small, clean, dry beaker (50 mL) that is easy to handle. Then pour the liquid from the small beaker into the buret. This simple method will prevent unnecessary spillage. Never pour any unused liquid back into the reagent bottle.

d. Fill the buret with the liquid and then open the stopcock to release enough liquid to fill the tip below the stopcock and bring the level of the liquid within the scale. The height at which the liquid stands is then read accurately. Practice this procedure several times by pouring water into the buret and emptying it through the stopcock.

4. Notice that the surface of a liquid in the buret is slightly curved. It is concave if it wets the glass and convex if it does not wet the glass. Such a curved surface is called a meniscus. If a liquid wets the glass, read the bottom of the meniscus, as shown in **Figure 9.** This is the line *CB.* If you read the markings at the top of the meniscus, *AD,* you will get an incorrect reading. Locate the bottom of the meniscus and read the water level in your buret.

Figure 8

Stopcock

Figure 9

Buret reading: Student answer _____

_____

Laboratory Procedures *continued*

5. After you have taken your first buret reading, open the stopcock to release some of the liquid. Then read the buret again. The exact amount released is equal to the difference between your first and final buret reading. Practice measuring liquids by measuring 10 mL of water, using a graduated cylinder, a pipet, and a buret.

6. At the end of this part of the experiment, the equipment you store in the lab locker or drawer should be clean, dry, and arranged in an orderly fashion for the next lab experiment.

CAUTION: In many experiments, you will have to dispose of a liquid chemical at the end of a lab. Always ask your teacher about the correct method of disposal. In many instances, liquid chemicals can be washed down the sink's drain by diluting them with plenty of tap water. Toxic chemicals should be handled only by your teacher. All apparatus should be washed, rinsed, and dried.

7. Remember to wash your hands thoroughly with soap at the end of this part of the experiment.

PART 6—FILTRATION

MATERIALS

- beaker, 250 mL (2)
- Bunsen burner and related equipment
- evaporating dish
- filter paper
- fine sand
- funnel
- glass stirring rod
- gloves
- iron ring
- lab apron
- ring stand
- safety goggles
- sodium chloride
- sparker
- wash bottle
- water
- wire gauze, ceramic-centered

Procedure

Figure 10

1. Sometimes liquids contain particles of insoluble solids that are present either as impurities or as precipitates formed by the interaction of the chemicals used in the experiment. If the particles are denser than water, they soon sink to the bottom. Most of the clear, supernatant liquid above the solid may be poured off without disturbing the precipitate. This method of separation is known as decantation.

2. Fine particles, or particles that settle slowly, are often separated from a liquid by filtration. Support a funnel on a small ring on the ring stand, as shown in **Figure 10.** Use a beaker to collect the filtrate. Adjust the funnel so that the stem of the funnel just touches the inside wall of the beaker.

3. Fold a circular piece of filter paper along its diameter, then fold it again to form a quadrant, as shown in **Figure 11.** Separate the folds of the filter paper, with three thickness on one side and one on the other; then place the resulting filter paper cone in the funnel.

Figure 11

Filter paper folded in half

Filter paper folded in quarters

Filter paper ready for funnel

Filter paper in funnel

Name _____ Class _____ Date _____

Laboratory Procedures *continued*

The funnel should be wet before you insert the filter paper. Use your plastic wash bottle to wet the funnel and the filter paper. Press the edges of the filter paper firmly against the sides of the funnel so no air can get between the funnel and the filter paper while the liquid is being filtered. *EXCEPTION: A filter should not be wetted with water when the liquid to be filtered does not mix with water. Why?*

Because the liquid does not mix with water, a filter paper wetted with water

will not allow the liquid to pass through.

4. Dissolve 2 or 3 g of sodium chloride in a beaker containing about 50 mL of water, and then stir into the solution an equal volume of fine sand. Filter out the sand by pouring the mixture into the filter, observing the following suggestions:

a. The filter paper should not extend above the edge of the funnel. Use filter paper that leaves about 1 cm of the funnel exposed.

b. Do not completely fill the funnel. It must never overflow.

c. Try to establish a water column in the stem of the funnel to eliminate air bubbles, and then add the liquid quickly enough to keep the mixture level about 1 cm from the top of the filter paper.

d. When a liquid is poured from a beaker, it may adhere to the glass and run down the outside wall. This may be avoided by holding a stirring rod against the lip of the beaker, as shown in **Figure 10** on the previous page. The liquid will run down the rod and drop off into the funnel without running down the outside of the beaker. The sand is retained on the filter paper. What property of the sand enables it to be separated from the water by filtration?

The sand is insoluble in water.

What does the filtrate contain?

The filtrate contains salt dissolved in water.

5. The salt can be recovered from the filtrate by pouring the filtrate into an evaporating dish and evaporating it over a low flame nearly to dryness. **Figure 12** shows a correct setup for evaporation.

CAUTION: When using a Bunsen burner, confine loose clothing and long hair. Wear your safety goggles, lab apron, and heat-resistant gloves.

Laboratory Procedures *continued*

6. Remove the flame as soon as the liquid begins to spatter. Shut off the burner. What property of salt prevents it from being separated from the water by filtration?

Salt is soluble in water.

7. All equipment should be clean, dry, and put away in an orderly fashion for the next lab experiment. Be sure that the valve on the gas jet is completely shut off. Make certain that the filter papers and sand are disposed of in the waste jars or containers and not down the sink. Remember to wash your hands thoroughly with soap at the end of each laboratory period.

Figure 12

Evaporating dish

Wire gauze (ceramic-centered)

Low flame

Analysis

Answer the following questions in complete sentences.

1. Organizing Ideas As soon as you enter the lab, what safety equipment should you put on immediately?

Safety goggles, gloves, and lab apron should be put on.

2. Organizing Ideas Before doing an experiment, what should you read and discuss with your teacher?

All safety precautions in the procedures should be read and discussed with

the teacher.

3. Organizing Ideas Before you light a burner, what safety precautions should always be followed?

Safety goggles and lab apron should be worn. Long hair should be tied back

and loose clothing should be confined. One should know the locations of fire

extinguishers, fire blankets, and sand buckets and the procedure for using

them in case of a fire.

4. Organizing Ideas What immediate action should you take when the flame of your burner is burning inside the base of the barrel?

Immediately turn off the gas at the gas valve, and then allow the barrel of

the burner to cool.

5. Organizing Ideas What type of flame is preferred for laboratory work, and why?

The nonluminous flame with the light-blue inner cone is preferred because it

burns hotter and cleaner than the yellow luminous flame.

6. Analyzing Ideas When inserting glass tubing, why is it important that you wear safety goggles and gloves and that you cover the tubing and stopper with protective pads of cloth?

These precautions are necessary to prevent personal injuries, such as cuts, if

the tubing should break. Eyes also need protection in case the tubing should

break and scatter fragments.

7. Analyzing Ideas What do you think might be a common cause of fires in lab drawers or lockers?

Putting away hot apparatus before it has had a chance to cool.

8. Analyzing Ideas Why are broken glassware, chemicals, matches, and other laboratory debris never discarded in a wastepaper basket?

This is an important safety precaution against fires and personal injuries,

such as cuts from broken glass or chemical poisoning, to anyone who empties

the wastepaper basket.

9. Organizing Ideas List the safety precautions that should be observed when inserting or removing glass tubing from a rubber stopper or rubber hose.

a. **The ends of the glass tubing must be fire polished.**

b. **A lubricant should be used on the ends of the tubing.**

c. **Always aim the glass tubing away from the palm of the hand that holds**

   the stopper or hose.

d. **Put folded cloth pads between both hands and the glass tubing, or wear**

   leather gloves.

e. **Use a gentle twisting motion when inserting the tubing.**

f. **Immediately remove the tubing at the end of an experiment.**

g. **Follow the same precautions for removal as specified for insertion.**

Laboratory Procedures *continued*

10. **Analyzing Ideas** Why should you never touch chemicals with your hands?

Some chemicals readily pass through the skin into the bloodstream. Some

chemicals are extremely corrosive.

11. **Organizing Ideas** What precaution can help prevent chemical contamination in reagent bottles?

Never return unused chemicals to reagent bottles.

12. **Analyzing Ideas** Why are chemicals and hot objects never placed directly on the balance pan?

They can permanently damage the surface of the balance pan and affect the

accuracy of mass measurements.

13. **Organizing Ideas** List three pieces of equipment used in the laboratory for measuring small quantities of liquids. What is the correct procedure for filling a buret with liquid?

Graduated cylinders, pipets, and burets are used to measure liquids. To fill a

buret, first pour the liquid into a small beaker that is easy to handle. Then

pour the liquid from the small beaker into the buret.

14. **Organizing Ideas** What is the rule about the size of filter paper to be used with a funnel?

The filter paper should not extend above the edge of the funnel.

Use filter paper that leaves about 1 cm of the funnel exposed above the edge

of the filter cone.

15. **Organizing Ideas** How can a liquid be transferred from a beaker to a funnel without spattering and without running down the outside wall of the beaker?

A stirring rod may be held against the lip of the beaker. When you pour, the

liquid will cling to the rod, run down it, and drop into the funnel.

Laboratory Procedures *continued*

16. Organizing Ideas Describe the condition of all lab equipment at the end of an experiment. What should be checked before you leave the lab?

All equipment that is stored in the lab locker or drawer should be completely

cool, clean, dry, and arranged in an orderly fashion for the next lab experi-

ment. Check to see that the valve on the gas jet is completely turned off.

17. Organizing Ideas What is the correct procedure for removing a solid reagent from its container in preparation for its use in an experiment?

First, read the label on the reagent bottle before removing any of its con-

tents. Use a clean spatula to remove the approximate quantity needed. Place

the reagent on a piece of glazed paper or in a clean, premassed container, as

directed by your teacher. Never touch the chemical with your hands, and

never pour the chemical from its original bottle into another container.

Dispose of any unused chemical as directed by your teacher. Never return it

to its original container.

18. Organizing Ideas What is the correct procedure for removing a liquid reagent from its container in preparation for its use in an experiment?

First, read the label on the reagent bottle before removing any of its con-

tents. After removing the glass stopper from a reagent bottle, never place

the stopper on the lab table. Carefully pour the approximate amount of

chemical needed into a small, clean, dry beaker (50 mL) that is easy to

handle. Then carefully transfer the liquid into the appropriate device to

measure the volume needed. The same cautions for using a solid reagent also

apply to liquids.

19. Analyzing Ideas Why is it important to use low flame when evaporating water from a recovered filtrate?

A low flame will heat the evaporating dish and its contents gently. This will

prevent the evaporating dish from cracking and will also keep the recovered

solid from burning.

Laboratory Procedures *continued*

General Conclusions

SAFETY CHECK

Identify the following safety symbols:

a. eye safety

b. heating and fire safety

c. clothing protection

d. chemical safety

e. glassware safety

f. hand safety

g. explosion danger

h. caustic substances

i. waste disposal

j. electrical safety

LABELING

Practice labeling a chemical container or bottle by filling in the appropriate information that is missing from the label pictured on the following page. Use 6 M sodium hydroxide (NaOH) as the solution to be labeled. (Hint: 6 M sodium hydroxide is a caustic and corrosive solution, and it can be considered potentially as hazardous as 6 M HCl.)

Laboratory Procedures *continued*

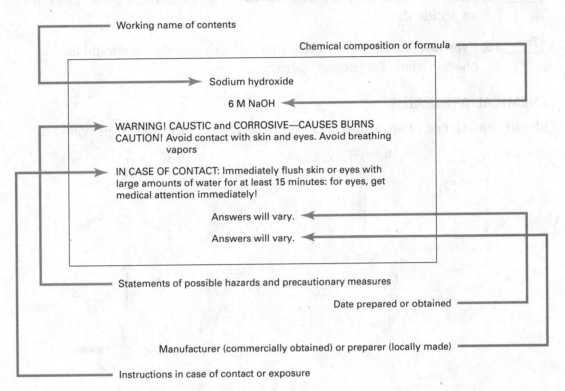

SAMPLE LABEL

Working name of contents

Chemical composition or formula

Sodium hydroxide

6 M NaOH

WARNING! CAUSTIC and CORROSIVE—CAUSES BURNS
CAUTION! Avoid contact with skin and eyes. Avoid breathing
vapors

IN CASE OF CONTACT: Immediately flush skin or eyes with
large amounts of water for at least 15 minutes: for eyes, get
medical attention immediately!

Answers will vary.

Answers will vary.

Statements of possible hazards and precautionary measures

Date prepared or obtained

Manufacturer (commercially obtained) or preparer (locally made)

Instructions in case of contact or exposure

TRUE OR FALSE

Read the following statements and indicate whether they are true or false. Place
your answer in the space next to the statement.

__True__ **1.** Never work alone in the laboratory.

__True__ **2.** Never lay the stopper of a reagent bottle on the lab table.

__False__ **3.** At the end of an experiment, in order to save the school's money, save
all excess chemicals and pour them back into their stock bottles.

__False__ **4.** The quickest and safest way to heat a material in a test tube is by
concentrating the flame on the bottom of the test tube.

__True__ **5.** Use care in selecting glassware for high-temperature heating.
Glassware should be Pyrex or a similar heat-treated type.

__True__ **6.** A mortar and pestle should be used for grinding only one substance at
a time.

__False__ **7.** Safety goggles protect your eyes from particles and chemical injuries.
It is completely safe to wear contact lenses under them while performing experiments.

__True__ **8.** Never use the wastepaper basket for disposal of chemicals.

_____**False**_____ **9.** First aid kits may be used by anyone to give emergency treatment after an accident.

_____**True**_____ **10.** Eyewash and facewash fountains and safety showers should be checked daily for proper operation.

CHEMICAL APPARATUS

Identify each piece of apparatus. Place your answers in the spaces provided.

a. __beaker_____

b. __graduated cylinder_____

c. __spatula_____

d. __pipestem triangle_____

e. __funnel_____

f. __evaporating dish_____

g. __Erlenmeyer flask_____

h. __Bunsen burner_____

i. __test tube_____

j. __ceramic-centered wire gauze_

k. __crucible and cover_____

l. __mortar and pestle_____

Accuracy and Precision in Measurements

Teacher Notes

TIME REQUIRED 60 min

SKILLS ACQUIRED

    Collecting data
    Communicating
    Experimenting
    Identifying patterns
    Inferring
    Interpreting
    Measuring
    Organizing and analyzing data

RATING

Easy ◄——— 1   2   3   4 ———► Hard

    Teacher Prep–2
    Student Set-Up–2
    Concept Level–3
    Clean Up–1

THE SCIENTIFIC METHOD

Make Observations Students collect data.

Analyze the Results Analysis question 1 to 14

Draw Conclusions Conclusions question 1

Communicate the Results Analysis questions 1 to 14

SAFETY CAUTIONS

Read all safety cautions, and discuss them with your students.

• Safety goggles and a lab apron must be worn at all times.

• Tie back loose hair and long clothing when working in the lab.

TIPS AND TRICKS

Some students will already know how to read volume graduations on a graduated cylinder and use the balance. They may need help only in reading them more precisely.

    Students may have difficulty understanding the difference between accuracy and precision. You might use the analogy of the dart board. If darts puncture the board over a large circular area surrounding the bull's eye, the shots may be considered to be accurate because an average of the positions of all the shots would come close to the position of the bull's eye. However, the shots would not be precise, because they are not close together. On the other hand, a distribution of shots such that they are clustered in a small area below the bull's eye might be considered precise because they are close together, but not accurate, because their positions do not average to that of the bull's eye.

Impress upon students that an estimate of uncertainty is a necessary part of every experimental measurement, that the uncertainty determines the number of significant digits the measurement can have, and that the degree of uncertainty, as measurements are added and subtracted, multiplied and divided, must match that in the original measurements.

The general rule for estimating a measurement is to estimate to one-tenth of the smallest readable division on the measuring apparatus.

DISPOSAL

The metal shot can be dried and reused in each class.

Skills Practice

Accuracy and Precision in Measurements

In this experiment, you will determine the volume of a liquid in two different ways and compare the results. You will also calculate the density of a metal, using your measurements of its mass and volume.

$$D = \frac{m}{V}$$

You will compare your result with the accepted value found in a the handbook. The experimental error and percentage error in each part of the experiment will be calculated.

The *experimental error* is calculated by subtracting the accepted value from the observed or experimental value, as follows:

$$Experimental\ error = Experimental\ value - Accepted\ value$$

The *percentage error* is calculated according to the following equation:

$$Percentage\ error = \frac{Experimental\ value - Accepted\ value}{Accepted\ value} \times 100$$

The sign of the experimental error and the percentage error may be either positive (the experimental result is too high) or negative (the experimental result is too low).

You will determine the average value for the density of a metal by averaging the values obtained by the entire class. Using this value, you will calculate the experimental error and percentage error in the class average.

OBJECTIVES

Use experimental measurements in calculations.

Organize data by compiling it in tables.

Compute an average value from class data.

Recognize the importance of accuracy and precision in scientific measurements.

Relate the reliability of experimental data to uncertainty and percent error.

MATERIALS

- 15 cm plastic ruler
- 25 mL graduated cylinder
- 100 mL beaker
- 100 mL graduated cylinder
- balance
- metal shot (aluminum, copper, lead)
- thermometer, nonmercury, 0–100°C

Accuracy and Precision in Measurements *continued*

Procedure

After completing each part of the experiment, record your observations in the appropriate data table. Recording data anywhere else increases the probability of recording an inaccurate value.

PART 1

1. Examine the centimeter scale of the plastic ruler. What are the smallest divisions?

The smallest divisions on the ruler are millimeters.

2. You can estimate a measurement to one-tenth of the smallest division on a measuring apparatus. To what fraction of a centimeter can you estimate with your plastic ruler?

You can estimate to 0.01 cm.

3. The uncertainty in a measurement is ± one-half of the smallest division. What is the uncertainty in a measurement made with your plastic ruler?

The uncertainty is ± 0.05 cm.

4. Using the ruler, measure the inside diameter of the 100 mL graduated cylinder. Similarly, measure the inside height of the cylinder to the 50 mL mark. Record these measurements in **Data Table 1.**

Data Table 1	
Inside diameter of graduated cylinder	**2.50 cm**
Inside height of graduated cylinder	**9.31 cm**

PART 2

5. Examine the gram scale of the balance. What are the smallest divisions?

The smallest divisions are centigrams.

To what fraction of a gram can you estimate with a centigram balance?

You should be able to estimate to 0.001 g.

6. Examine the graduations on a 25 mL graduated cylinder, and determine the smallest fraction of a milliliter to which you could make a measurement. Does this match the *uncertainty* of a measurement made with a 100 mL graduated cylinder?

Most 25 mL cylinders are subdivided by 0.5 mL graduations, whereas 100 mL

cylinders are subdivided by 1 mL graduations. The uncertainties of measure-

ments using the two cylinders do not match (± 0.25 mL for the 25 mL cylin-

der and ± 0.5 mL for the 100 mL cylinder).

7. Using the balance, measure the mass of the dry 25 mL cylinder. Record the mass in **Data Table 2.**

8. Fill the beaker half full of water, and measure its temperature to the nearest degree. Look up the density of water for this temperature in your textbook, and record in **Data Table 2** both the temperature and water density.

9. Fill your graduated cylinder with water to a level between 10 and 25 mL; accurately read and record the volume. Measure the mass of the water plus the cylinder, then record this value in **Data Table 2.** Save the water in the graduated cylinder for use in **Part 3.**

Data Table 2		
Mass of empty graduated cylinder	**42.39**	g
Temperature of water	**25.0**	°C
Density of water	**0.997**	g/cm³
Volume of water	**13.80**	mL
Mass of graduated cylinder + water	**55.98**	g

Name _____ Class _____ Date _____

| **Accuracy and Precision in Measurements** *continued*

PART 3

10. Add a sufficient quantity of the assigned metal shot (aluminum, copper, or lead) to the cylinder containing the water (saved from **Part 2**) to increase the volume by at least 5 mL. Measure the volume and then the mass of the metal shot, water, and cylinder. Record your measurements in **Data Table 3.**

Data Table 3		
Volume of water (from **Part 2**)	**13.80**	mL
Mass of water + graduated cylinder (from **Part 2**)	**55.98**	g
Volume of metal + water	**20.25**	mL
Mass of metal + water + graduated cylinder	**73.98**	g

DISPOSAL

11. Clean up all apparatus and your lab station. Return equipment to its proper place. Wash your hands thoroughly with soap before you leave the lab and after all work is finished.

Analysis

Show all your calculations.

Part 1

1. Organizing Data Calculate the volume of the cylinder to the 50.0 mL graduation ($V = \pi \times r^2 \times h$).

$$V = \pi\, r^2\, h = \pi \times \left(\frac{2.50\ \text{cm}}{2}\right)^2 \times 9.31\ \text{cm} = 45.7\ \text{cm}^3$$

2. Inferring Conclusions Assume the accepted value for the volume of the cylinder is 50.0 cm³. Calculate the experimental error and percentage error.

Experimental error: 45.7 cm³ − 50.0 cm³ = 4.3 cm³

Percentage error: $\dfrac{4.3\ \text{cm}^3}{50.0\ \text{cm}^3} \times 100 = 8.6\%$

Part 2

3. Organizing Data Calculate the mass of water as measured by the balance.

(Mass of cylinder + water) − mass of cylinder = mass of water

55.98 g − 42.39 g = 13.59 g of water

Accuracy and Precision in Measurements *continued*

4. **Organizing Data** Calculate the mass of the water from its measured volume and its density ($m = D \times V$).

$$m = D \times V = 0.997 \text{ g/cm}^3 \times 13.80 \text{ cm}^3 = 13.8 \text{ g}$$

5. **Inferring Conclusions** Using the mass of water determined by the use of the balance as the *accepted value*, calculate the experimental error and percentage error in the mass determined using the volume and density.

Experimental error: $13.80 \text{ g} - 13.59 \text{ g} = 0.21 \text{ g}$

Percentage error: $\dfrac{0.21 \text{ g}}{13.59 \text{ g}} \times 100 = 1.5\%$

Part 3

6. **Organizing Data** Determine the volume of the metal, using your measurement of the volume of water displaced by the metal.

Volume of metal $= 20.25 \text{ mL} - 13.80 \text{ mL} = 6.45 \text{ mL} = 6.45 \text{ cm}^3$

7. **Organizing Data** Using your measurements in **Data Table 3**, determine the mass of the metal.

Mass of metal $= 73.98 \text{ g} - 55.98 \text{ g} = 18.00 \text{ g}$

8. **Organizing Data** Calculate the density of the metal.

Density of metal $= \dfrac{18.00 \text{ g}}{6.45 \text{ cm}^3} = 2.79 \text{ g/cm}^3$

9. **Inferring Conclusions** In a handbook, your textbook, or on-line, look up the density of the metal you used. (In SI, the density of liquids and solids is equal to the specific gravity.) Calculate the experimental error and percentage error for the density of the metal shot you determined in item **8.**

Experimental error: $2.79 \text{ g/cm}^3 - 2.70 \text{ g/cm}^3 = 0.10 \text{ g/cm}^3$

Percentage error: $\dfrac{0.10 \text{ g/cm}^3}{2.70 \text{ g/cm}^3} \times 100 = 4\%$

Part 4

10. **Organizing Conclusions** Record in the table below five values obtained by you and your classmates for the density of the *same metal.*

Group number	Density (g/cm³)
1	2.79
2	3.00
3	2.95
4	2.79
5	2.81

Name _____ Class _____ Date _____

| **Accuracy and Precision in Measurements** *continued*

11. Evaluating Conclusions Calculate the average density (*D*) of the five results.

$$D = \frac{2.79 + 3.00 + 2.95 + 2.79 + 2.81}{5} = 2.87 \text{ g/cm}^3$$

12. Inferring Conclusions Calculate the experimental error and the percentage error for the average density of the metal shot.

Experimental error: $2.87 \text{ g/cm}^3 - 2.70 \text{ g/cm}^3 = 0.17 \text{ g/cm}^3$

Percentage error: $\frac{0.17 \text{ g/cm}^3}{2.70 \text{ g/cm}^3} \times 100 = 6.3\%$

13. Evaluating Methods What value of a measurement must be known if the accuracy of an experimental measurement is to be determined?

The accepted value of a measurement must be known.
_____

_____

14. Evaluating Methods What are the possible sources of experimental errors in this experiment?

Sources of experimental errors include inaccurate observations and
_____

imperfections in apparatus design.
_____

Conclusions

1. Evaluating Conclusions Sarah and Jamal determined the density of a liquid three times. The values they obtained were 2.84 g/cm³, 2.85 g/cm³, and 2.80 g/cm³. The accepted value is known to be 2.40 g/cm³.

a. Are the values that Sarah and Jamal determined precise? Explain.

Yes, the measurements are in close agreement.
_____

_____

b. Are the values accurate? Explain.

No, they are not close enough to the real value.
_____

_____

Accuracy and Precision in Measurements *continued*

c. Calculate the percentage error for each density.

Percentage error:

$$\frac{2.84 \text{ g/cm}^3 - 2.40 \text{ g/cm}^3}{2.40 \text{ g/cm}^3} \times 100 = 18.3\%$$

$$\frac{2.85 \text{ g/cm}^3 - 2.40 \text{ g/cm}^3}{2.40 \text{ g/cm}^3} \times 100 = 18.8\%$$

$$\frac{2.80 \text{ g/cm}^3 - 2.40 \text{ g/cm}^3}{2.40 \text{ g/cm}^3} \times 100 = 16.7\%$$

Accuracy and Precision of Measurement—the Student

chemical... and physical... errors instead of stand...

$$\frac{2.85 \text{ g/cm}^3 - 3.10 \text{ g/cm}^3}{3.10 \text{ g/cm}^3} \times 100\% = -8.06\%$$

$$\frac{2.80 \text{ g/cm}^3 - 3.10 \text{ g/cm}^3}{3.10 \text{ g/cm}^3} \times 100\% = -12.9\%$$

Water of Hydration

Teacher Notes
TIME REQUIRED 60 min

SKILLS ACQUIRED
Collecting data
Experimenting
Identifying patterns
Inferring
Interpreting
Organizing and analyzing data

RATING

Easy ←——1——2——3——4——→ Hard

Teacher Prep–2
Student Set-Up–2
Concept Level–3
Clean Up–2

THE SCIENTIFIC METHOD

Make Observations Students collect mass data.

Analyze the Results Analysis questions 1 to 7 and Conclusions question 1

Draw Conclusions Conclusions questions 1 to 5

Communicate the Results Analysis questions 1 to 7 and Conclusions question 3

MATERIALS

If you don't have a desiccator, you can use clean, empty jars with wide mouths and tight lids, such as peanut butter jars. Put a layer of granular anhydrous calcium chloride on the bottom of the jar. Bend down the ends of pipe-stem triangles to act as legs. Place one triangle in each jar to hold a crucible securely.

Remind students that heated objects can be hot enough to burn, even if they look cool. Students should always use crucible tongs to handle crucibles and covers.

SAFETY CAUTIONS

Read all safety precautions and discuss them with your students.

• Safety goggles and a lab apron must be worn at all times.

• Remind students to confine loose clothing and long hair before lighting a burner.

TECHNIQUES TO DEMONSTRATE

Set up the ring stand, ring, and pipe-stem triangle with the crucible in place. Show students how to place the crucible cover slightly ajar. Turn on and adjust the burner flame to the small, hot flame that is needed to dehydrate the salt. Demonstrate how to use tongs to transfer the hot crucible to the desiccator.

TIPS AND TRICKS

- Caution students to prevent loss of some of the hydrate by leaving only a small opening between the crucible and cover. Also, the crucible should not be heated too strongly for the first few minutes, because some of the hydrate could be lost with the water vapor.

- The molar mass of anhydrous $MgSO_4$ is 120.37 g/mol.

DISPOSAL

Provide a labeled container for students to dispose of the rehydrated and anhydrous magnesium sulfate and any excess of the original compound. Later, redissolve the contents of the container in distilled water. Let the solutions evaporate until dry, and then recover the crystals for reuse next year. If students repeat the experiment using any of the hydrates listed in **General Conclusions 4,** dispose of all but the copper sulfate, $CuSO_4$, by dissolving the salts in water and pouring them down the drain. Dissolve $CuSO_4$ in water, add sufficient 1.0 M NaOH to precipitate the copper, and then filter. The filtrate should be adjusted to a pH of 5 to 9 and then poured down the drain. The precipitate can be dried and put in the trash.

Name _____ Class _____ Date _____

Water of Hydration

Many ionic compounds, when crystallized from an aqueous solution, will take up definite amounts of water as an integral part of their crystal structures. You can drive off this water of crystallization by heating the hydrated substance to convert it to its anhydrous form. Because the law of definite composition holds for crystalline hydrates, the number of moles of water driven off per mole of the anhydrous compound is a simple whole number. If the formula of the anhydrous compound is known, you can use your data to determine the formula of the hydrate.

OBJECTIVES

Determine that all the water has been driven from a hydrate by heating a sample to constant mass.

Use experimental data to calculate the number of moles of water released by a hydrate.

Infer the empirical formula of the hydrate from the formula of the anhydrous compound and experimental data.

MATERIALS

- balance, centigram
- Bunsen burner and related equipment
- crucible and cover
- desiccator
- iron ring
- magnesium sulfate, Epsom salts, hydrated crystals, $MgSO_4 \cdot nH_2O$
- pipe-stem triangle
- ring stand
- sparker
- spatula
- crucible tongs

Always wear safety goggles and a lab apron to protect your eyes and clothing. If you get a chemical in your eyes, immediately flush the chemical out at the eyewash station while calling to your teacher. Know the locations of the emergency lab shower and the eyewash station and the procedures for using them.

Do not touch any chemicals. If you get a chemical on your skin or clothing, wash the chemical off at the sink while calling to your teacher. Make sure you carefully read the labels and follow the precautions on all containers of chemicals that you use. If there are no precautions stated on the label, ask your teacher what precautions you should follow. Do not taste any chemicals or items used in the laboratory. Never return leftovers to their original containers; take only small amounts to avoid wasting supplies.

 Call your teacher in the event of a spill. Spills should be cleaned up promptly, according to your teacher's directions.

| **Water of Hydration** *continued*

🔥 **When using a Bunsen burner, confine long hair and loose clothing.** If your clothing catches on fire, WALK to the emergency lab shower and use it to put out the fire. Do not heat glassware that is broken, chipped, or cracked. Use tongs or a hot mitt to handle heated glassware and other equipment because hot glassware does not look hot.

Procedure

1. Throughout the experiment, handle the crucible and cover with clean crucible tongs only. Place the crucible and cover on the triangle as shown in **Figure A.** Position the cover slightly tipped, leaving only a small opening for any gases to escape. Preheat the crucible and its cover until the bottom of the crucible turns red.

CAUTION The crucible and cover are very hot after each heating. Remember to handle them only with tongs.

2. Using tongs, transfer the crucible and cover to a desiccator. Allow them to cool 5 min in the desiccator. Never place a hot crucible on a balance. When the crucible and cover are cool, determine their mass to the nearest 0.01 g. Record this mass in the **Data Table.**

3. Using a spatula, add approximately 5 g of magnesium sulfate hydrate crystals to the crucible. Determine the mass of the covered crucible and crystals to the nearest 0.01 g. Record this mass in the **Data Table.**

Crucible   Pipe-stem triangle

Figure A

4. Place the crucible with the magnesium sulfate hydrate on the triangle, and again position the cover so that there is a small opening. Too large an opening may allow the hydrate to spatter out of the crucible. Heat the crucible very gently with a low flame to avoid spattering any of the hydrate. Increase the temperature gradually for 2 or 3 min. Then, heat strongly, but not red-hot, for at least 5 min.

5. Using tongs, transfer the crucible, cover, and contents to the desiccator, and allow them to cool for 5 min. Then, using the same balance you used in Step **2,** determine their mass. Be sure the crucible is sufficiently cool, because heat can affect your measurement. Record the mass in the **Data Table.**

6. Again heat the covered crucible and contents strongly for 5 min. Allow the crucible, cover, and contents to cool in the desiccator, and then use the same balance as before to determine their mass. If the last two mass measurements differ by no more than 0.01 g, you may assume that all the water has been driven off. Otherwise, repeat the heating process until the mass no longer changes. Record this constant mass in your **Data Table.**

DISPOSAL

7. Clean all apparatus and your lab station. Return equipment to its proper place. Dispose of the $MgSO_4$ in your crucible as your teacher directs. Do not pour any chemicals down the drain or in the trash unless your teacher directs you to do so. Wash your hands thoroughly after all work is finished and before you leave the lab.

Data Table	
Mass of empty crucible and cover	**32.25 g**
Mass of crucible, cover, and magnesium sulfate hydrate	**37.25 g**
Mass of crucible, cover, and anhydrous magnesium sulfate after 1st heating	**34.73 g**
Mass of crucible, cover, and anhydrous magnesium sulfate after last heating	**34.72 g**

Analysis

1. Organizing Data Calculate the mass of anhydrous magnesium sulfate (the residue that remained after driving off the water). Record the mass in the **Calculations Table.**

34.72 g − 32.25 g = 2.47 g anhydrous $MgSO_4$ (mass after last heating)

2. Organizing Data Calculate the number of moles of anhydrous magnesium sulfate. Record the number of moles in the **Calculations Table.**

$$2.47 \text{ g} \times \frac{1 \text{ mol } MgSO_4}{120.37 \text{ g}} = 0.0205 \text{ mol anhydrous } MgSO_4$$

3. Organizing Data Calculate the mass of water driven off from the hydrate. Record the mass in the **Calculations Table.**

37.25 g − 34.72 g = 2.53 g H_2O

4. Organizing Data Calculate the number of moles of water driven off from the hydrate. Record the number of moles in the **Calculations Table.**

$$2.53 \text{ g} \times \frac{1 \text{ mol H}_2\text{O}}{18.02 \text{ g}} = 0.141 \text{ mol H}_2\text{O}$$

5. Organizing Ideas Write the equation for the reaction that occurred when you heated hydrated $MgSO_4$ in this experiment. Use the letter n to represent the number of moles of water driven off per mole of anhydrous magnesium sulfate.

$$MgSO_4 \cdot n\,H_2O(s) \rightarrow MgSO_4(s) + n\,H_2O(g)$$

6. Organizing Conclusions Using your answers to Calculations Items **2**, **4**, and **5**, determine the mole ratio of $MgSO_4$ to H_2O to the nearest whole number. Record the ratio in the **Calculations Table.**

$$\text{Mole ratio} = \frac{MgSO_4}{H_2O} = \frac{0.0205 \text{ mol}}{0.141 \text{ mol}} = \frac{1 \text{ mol MgSO}_4}{6.88 \text{ mol H}_2\text{O}}; 1:7$$

7. Organizing Conclusions Use your answer to Calculations Item **6** to write the formula for the magnesium sulfate hydrate. Record the formula in the **Calculations Table.**

$$MgSO_4 \cdot 7H_2O$$

Calculations Table	
Mass of anhydrous magnesium sulfate	2.47 g
Moles of anhydrous magnesium sulfate	0.0205 mol
Mass of water driven off from hydrate	2.53 g
Moles of water driven off from hydrate	0.141 mol
Mole ratio of anhydrous magnesium sulfate to water	$1.00:6.88$ ($1:7$)
Empirical formula of the hydrate	$MgSO_4 \cdot 7H_2O$

| Water of Hydration *continued*

Conclusions

1. Applying Conclusions The following results were obtained when a solid was heated by three different lab groups. In each case, the students observed that when they began to heat the solid, drops of a liquid formed on the sides of the test tube.

Lab group	Mass before heating	Mass after heating
1	1.48 g	1.26 g
2	1.64 g	1.40 g
3	2.08 g	1.78 g

a. Could the solid be a hydrate? What evidence supports your answer?

Yes, because after being heated the mass is less, indicating that some mass

was driven off. The mass loss was probably due to water being driven off

since drops of liquid were observed on the sides of the test tube.

_____

b. If, after heating, the solid has a molar mass of 208 g/mol and a formula of XY, what is the formula of the hydrate? Use **Lab group 1**'s results.

Moles of anhydrous salt (XY) = $1.26 \text{ g} \times \dfrac{1 \text{ mol}}{208 \text{ g}} = 0.00606 \text{ mol}$

mol H_2O = $0.22 \text{ g} \times \dfrac{1 \text{ mol}}{18.02 \text{ g}} = 0.012 \text{ mol}$

$\dfrac{\text{mol } H_2O}{\text{mol XY}} = \dfrac{0.012}{0.0061} = \dfrac{2}{1}$; the formula is $XY \cdot 2H_2O$

2. Applying Conclusions Some cracker tins include a glass vial of drying material in the lid to keep the crackers crisp. In many cases, the material is a mixture of magnesium sulfate and cobalt chloride indicator. As the magnesium sulfate absorbs moisture ($MgSO_4 \cdot H_2O + 6H_2O \rightarrow MgSO_4 \cdot 7H_2O$), the indicator changes color from blue to pink ($CoCl_2 \cdot 4H_2O + 2H_2O \rightarrow CoCl_2 \cdot 6H_2O$). When this drying mixture becomes totally pink, it can be restored if it is heated in an oven. What two changes are caused by the heating?

Heating removes some of the water of hydration from both the magnesium

sulfate drying agent and the cobalt chloride indicator. The mixture turns

back to a blue color, ready to absorb more moisture.

_____

_____

Water of Hydration *continued*

3. Applying Conclusions How does the experiment you performed exemplify the law of definite composition?

Every compound has the same elements in exactly the same proportion

by mass no matter what the size of the sample or its source. You can infer

that there always will be the same mass, and the same number of moles,

of water molecules present in each mole of magnesium sulfate heptahydrate.

_____

_____

_____

_____

4. Analyzing Methods Why did you use the same balance each time you measured the mass of the crucible and its contents?

There can be differences in balances. For the most accurate results, it's best

to use the same balance when comparing masses.

_____

5. Predicting Outcomes Use handbooks to investigate the properties of the compounds listed in the following table. Write answers to these questions in the table: Does the compound form a hydrate? How would you describe the appearance of the anhydrous compound? If your teacher approves, repeat the experimental procedure, using one of the listed compounds, and verify its hydrate formula. Explain any large deviation from the correct hydrate formula.

Name of Compound	Water of crystallization?	Appearance of anhydrous compound
Sodium carbonate	**yes**	**white powder**
Sodium sulfate	**yes**	**white powder**
Sodium aluminum sulfate	**yes**	**white powder**
Potassium chloride	**no**	**unchanged**
Magnesium chloride	**yes**	**white powder**
Copper sulfate	**yes**	**white powder**

Evidence for Chemical Change

Teacher Notes

TIME REQUIRED One 45-minute lab period

SKILLS ACQUIRED
Collecting data
Experimenting
Identifying patterns
Inferring
Interpreting
Measuring
Organizing and analyzing data

RATING
Easy ◄——— 1   2   3   4 ———► Hard

Teacher preparation–3
Student Setup–2
Concept level–2
Cleanup–2

THE SCIENTIFIC METHOD

Make Observations Students observe the results of different chemical reactions.

Analyze the Results Analysis questions 3, 4, 5, and 6.

Draw Conclusions Conclusions questions 1, 2, 3, and 4.

Communicate the Results Conclusions questions 3 and 4.

MATERIALS

Materials for this lab activity can be purchased from WARD'S. See the *Master Materials List* on the **One-Stop Planner** CD-ROM for ordering instructions.

In preparing 1 L of 1.0 M HCl solution, observe the required safety precautions. While stirring, slowly add 83 mL of concentrated HCl to enough distilled water to make 1 L of solution.

To prepare 1 L of 1.0 M copper(II) nitrate, dissolve 296 g of $Cu(NO_3)_2 \cdot 6H_2O$, or 242 g of $Cu(NO_3)_2 \cdot 3H_2O$, in enough distilled water to make 1.0 L of solution.

In preparing 1 L of 1.0 M sodium hydroxide, observe the required safety precautions. While stirring slowly, dissolve 40 g of NaOH in enough distilled water to make 1.0 L of solution.

SAFETY CAUTIONS

Wear safety safety goggles, a face shield, impermeable gloves, and a lab apron when you prepare the 1.0 M HCl and the 1.0 M NaOH solutions.

When making the HCl solution, work in a chemical fume hood known to be in operating condition, and have another person stand by to call for help in case of an emergency. Be sure you are within a 30-second walk from a safety shower and eyewash station known to be in good operating condition.

In case of a spill, use a dampened cloth or paper towels to mop up the spill. Then, rinse the cloth or towel in running water at the sink, wring it out until it is only damp, and put it in the trash. In the event of an acid or base spill, dilute the spilled liquid with water first, and then proceed as described.

Remind students of the following safety precautions:

- Always wear safety goggles and a lab apron to protect your eyes and clothing. If you get any chemical in your eyes, immediately flush the chemical out at the eyewash station while calling to your teacher. Know the location of the emergency lab shower and the eyewash stations and procedures for using them.

- Do not touch any chemicals. If you get a chemical on your skin or clothing, wash the chemical off at the sink while calling to your teacher. Make sure you carefully read the labels and follow the precautions on all containers of chemicals that you use. If there are no precautions stated on the label, ask your teacher what precautions you should follow. Do not taste any chemicals or items used in the laboratory. Never return leftovers to their original containers; take only small amounts to avoid wasting supplies.

- Call your teacher in the event of a spill. Spills should be cleaned up promptly according to your teacher's directions.

- When using a Bunsen burner, confine long hair and loose clothing. If your clothing catches on fire, WALK to the emergency lab shower, and use it to put out the fire. Do not heat glassware that is broken, chipped, or cracked. Use tongs or a hot mitt to handle heated glassware and other equipment because heated glassware does not look hot.

- Never put broken glass in a regular waste container. Broken glass should be disposed of properly.

DISPOSAL

Combine all solutions and precipitates containing copper. Add 1.0 M NaOH slowly while stirring until all the copper has precipitated as the hydroxide. Filter the liquid to remove the precipitate. After drying the precipitate, put it into the trash. Slowly, while stirring, add all the waste HCl solution to the filtrate. Then adjust the pH of this mixture to between 5 and 9 by adding 1.0 M acid or base, as necessary. Then pour the neutralized mixture down the drain.

TECHNIQUES TO DEMONSTRATE

Show the students the proper method for using a pipet.

Review how to read a meniscus.

Demonstrate the proper setup and use of the hot-water bath.

TIPS AND TRICKS

Thin-stemmed pipets or dropper bottles may be used to dispense the solutions.

Emphasize the importance of making the marks on the test tube carefully to insure accurate mesurements. You may wish to set up several hot-water baths in the room to eliminate student use of the burner.

Analysis

Encourage students to make careful observations using all their senses (except taste). Remind them to look for changes that indicate that a new substance has formed and to record their observations immediately.

Name _____ Class _____ Date _____

Evidence for Chemical Change

One way of knowing that a chemical change has occurred is to observe that the properties of the products are different from those of the reactants. A new product can then become a reactant in another chemical reaction. In this experiment, you will observe a sequence of changes that occur when a solution that begins as copper(II) nitrate is subjected to a series of different reactions. All of the reactions will take place in the same test tube. At each step, you will look for evidence that a new substance has formed as a result of a chemical change. You will also observe energy changes and relate them to chemical reactions.

OBJECTIVES

Observe evidence that a chemical change has taken place.

Infer from observations that a new substance has been formed.

Identify and record observations that show energy is involved in chemical change.

Observe the color and solubility of some substances.

Describe reactions by writing word equations.

MATERIALS

- aluminum wire, 12 cm
- beaker, 100 mL
- Bunsen burner and related equipment
- copper(II) nitrate, 1.0 M
- glass stirring rod
- gloves
- HCl, 1.0 M
- iron ring
- lab apron

- lab marker
- NaOH, 1.0 M
- ring stand
- ruler
- safety goggles
- test tube, 13 mm × 100 mm
- test-tube rack
- wire gauze, ceramic-centered

Always wear safety goggles and a lab apron to protect your eyes and clothing. If you get a chemical in your eyes, immediately flush the chemical out at the eyewash station while calling to your teacher. Know the location of the emergency lab shower and the eyewash station and the procedures for using them.

Do not touch any chemicals. If you get a chemical on your skin or clothing, wash the chemical off at the sink while calling to your teacher. Make sure you carefully read the labels and follow the precautions on all containers of chemicals that you use. If there are no precautions stated on the label, ask your teacher what precautions to follow. Do not taste any chemicals or items used in the laboratory. Never return leftover chemicals to their original containers; take only small amounts to avoid wasting supplies.

Call your teacher in the event of a spill. Spills should be cleaned up promptly, according to your teacher's directions.

Acids and bases are corrosive. If an acid or base spills onto your skin or clothing, wash the area immediately with running water. Call your teacher in the event of an acid spill. Acid or base spills should be cleaned up promptly.

Never put broken glass in a regular waste container. Broken glass should be disposed of separately according to your teacher's instructions.

Do not heat glassware that is broken, chipped, or cracked. Use tongs or a hot mitt to handle heated glassware and other equipment because hot glassware does not always look hot.

When using a Bunsen burner, confine long hair and loose clothing. If your clothing catches on fire, WALK to the emergency lab shower and use it to put out the fire.

When heating a substance in a test tube, the mouth of the test tube should point away from where you and others are standing. Watch the test tube at all times to prevent the contents from boiling over.

Procedure

1. Put on safety goggles, gloves, and a lab apron.

2. Place 50 mL of water into the 100 mL beaker and heat it until boiling. This will be the water bath you will use in **Step 6.**

3. While the water bath is heating, use the lab marker and ruler to make three marks on the test tube that are 1 cm apart. Make the marks starting at the bottom of the test tube and moving toward the top.

4. Add 1.0 M copper(II) nitrate to the first mark on the test tube, as shown in **Figure 1.**

5. Add 1.0 M sodium hydroxide (NaOH) up to the second mark on the test tube, as shown in **Figure 2. CAUTION: Sodium hydroxide is corrosive. Be certain to wear safety goggles, gloves, and a lab apron. Avoid contact with skin and eyes. If any of this solution should spill on you, immediately flush the area with water and then notify your teacher.**

Mix the solutions with the stirring rod. Rinse the stirring rod thoroughly before setting it down on the lab table. Touch the bottom of the outside of the test tube to see if energy has been released. The copper-containing product in the test tube is copper(II) hydroxide. The other product is sodium nitrate. Record the changes that occur in the test tube in the space provided below.

Observations:

A blue precipitate is formed. Energy is evolved. _____

_____

Evidence for Chemical Change *continued*

| **Figure 1** | **Figure 2** | **Figure 3** |

6. Put the test tube into the water bath you prepared in **Step 2**. Heat it until no more changes occur. The products of this reaction are copper(II) oxide and water. Record the changes that occur in the test tube.

Observations:

The precipitate turns black. _____

7. Remove the test tube from the hot-water bath. Turn off the burner. Cool the test tube and its contents for 2 min in room-temperature water. Add 1.0 M hydrochloric acid (HCl) to the third mark, as shown in **Figure 3**.

CAUTION: Hydrochloric acid is corrosive. Be certain to wear safety goggles, gloves, and a lab apron. Avoid contact with skin and eyes. Avoid breathing vapors. If any of this solution should spill on you, immediately flush the area with water and then notify your teacher.

Mix with the stirring rod. Rinse the stirring rod.

The new products are copper(II) chloride and water. Record the changes that occur in the test tube.

Observations:

The precipitate dissolves and the solution turns green. _____

_____

_____

Evidence for Chemical Change *continued*

8. Place a 12-cm piece of aluminum wire in the test tube. Leave it until no reaction is observed. Touch the bottom of the test tube to check for temperature change. Two reactions take place. Copper(II) chloride and aluminum produce copper and aluminium chloride. The aluminum also reacts with the hydrochloric acid to form hydogen and aluminum chloride. Record the changes that occur in the test tube.

Observations:

The green color disappears and a dark reddish solid forms on the wire.

Energy is evolved. Bubbles are produced.

_____

9. Remove the wire from the test tube. Compare the copper formed to a sample of copper wire. Record your observations.

Observations:

The color is similar, but the shape and form are not.

_____

_____

10. Clean all apparatus and your lab station. Return equipment to its proper place. Dispose of chemicals and solutions in the containers designated by your teacher. Do not pour any chemicals down the drain or put them in the trash unless your teacher directs you to do so. Wash your hands thoroughly after all work is finished and before you leave the lab.

Analysis

1. Organizing Ideas What are some causes of chemical changes?

Combining chemicals, adding energy.

_____

2. Organizing Ideas In what two ways is energy involved in chemical change? Cite some specific instances from this experiment.

(1) Energy initiates chemical change: changing copper(II) hydroxide to

copper(II) oxide. (2) Energy is evolved during chemical change: copper(II)

nitrate + sodium hydroxide and aluminum + copper(II) chloride.

_____

Evidence for Chemical Change *continued*

3. Analyzing Information Identify all of the substances that are used or produced in this experiment. Distinguish between elements and compounds.

Elements: Al, Cu, H_2; compounds: $Cu(NO_3)_2$, NaOH, $Cu(OH)_2$, CuO, HCl,

$CuCl_2$, $AlCl_3$.

4. Analyzing Methods In the last step of the experiment, where is the aluminum chloride? How could you recover it?

Aluminum chloride is in the solution. Evaporate the water.

5. Inferring Conclusions What is the color of solutions of copper compounds?

Blue or green.

6. Analyzing Results Which substances involved in this experiment dissolve in water? Which do not dissolve?

Soluble: copper(II) nitrate, sodium hydroxide, hydrogen chloride, copper(II)

chloride, aluminum chloride.

Insoluble: copper(II) hydroxide, copper(II) oxide, copper metal, aluminum

metal.

7. Organizing Conclusions Refer to the procedure steps in the experiment, and complete the following word equations.

a. copper(II) nitrate + sodium hydroxide →
   copper(II) hydroxide + sodium nitrate

b. copper(II) hydroxide + energy →
   copper(II) oxide + water

c. copper(II) oxide + hydrochloric acid →
   copper(II) chloride + water

d. copper(II) chloride + aluminum →
   copper + aluminum chloride

e. hydrochloric acid + aluminum →
   hydrogen + aluminum chloride

Evidence for Chemical Change *continued*

Conclusions

1. Analyzing Information List four types of observations that indicate when a chemical change has occurred.

formation of a precipitate, color change, formation of a gas, evolution of

energy

2. Relating Ideas The chemical conversion of one product into another useful product is the basis for recycling. Explain how the type of reactions you observed in this experiment could be useful in the recycling of copper.

Copper metal was used in the preparation of the original copper(II) nitrate

solution. After several conversions, copper metal was again recovered.

3. Analyzing Conclusions Describe the advantages and disadvantages of recycling metals as was done in this experiment.

Advantages: pure metal is obtained from a compound, and the reaction is

done in one vessel.

Disadvantages: the reactions take time and may be expensive, and the waste

products of recovery may cause pollution.

Boyle's Law

Teacher Notes

TIME REQUIRED 30 minutes

SKILLS ACQUIRED
Collecting data
Communicating
Experimenting
Identifying patterns
Inferring
Interpreting
Measuring
Organizing and analyzing data

RATING

Easy ←——— 1   2   3   4 ———→ Hard

Teacher preparation–2
Student Setup–2
Concept level–2
Cleanup–1

THE SCIENTIFIC METHOD

Make Observations Students observe the results of applying pressure to a confined gas.

Analyze the Results Analysis questions 1 to 6 and Conclusions question 2.

Draw Conclusions Conclusions questions 1 to 3.

Communicate the Results Analysis questions 1 to 6 and Conclusions question 1.

MATERIALS

Check each apparatus for possible leaks. If the apparatus leaks, the piston will not return to its original position regardless of the number of times you twist the head. The most probable source of leakage is the bottom end of the syringe where the needle is normally attached.

Inserting a thread between the piston head and syringe barrel makes adjustment of the apparatus easier.

Each weight should be approximately 500 g. Less mass provides too small a change in volume. Greater mass may cause the pressure to be so excessive that air will begin to escape around the gasket. 500 g weights are ideal. All weights used by one lab group should be the same.

SAFETY CAUTIONS

Read all safety precautions, and discuss them with your students.

• Safety goggles and a lab apron must be worn at all times.

DISPOSAL

None

TIPS AND TRICKS

Show students how to give the piston several twists each time they change the pressure. The frictional force is significant, but if the piston is twisted until a stable volume is reached, reliable data should be obtained. Show students how to stack the weights carefully so that the pile is stable.

You may wish to have students calculate the uncertainty of the volumes and plot these on the graph of volume versus pressure. This could lead to a discussion about uncertainty and experimental error. In addition, it may help students appreciate why a line which does not actually go through every point is nevertheless an accurate representation of the data.

Boyle's Law

According to Boyle's law, the volume of a fixed amount of dry gas is inversely proportional to the pressure if the temperature is constant. Boyle's law may be stated mathematically as $P \propto \dfrac{1}{V}$ or $PV = k$ (where k is a constant). Notice that for Boyle's law to apply, two variables that affect gas behavior must be held constant: the amount of gas and the temperature.

   In this experiment, you will vary the pressure of air contained in a syringe and measure the corresponding change in volume. Because it is often impossible to determine relationships by just looking at data in a table, you will plot graphs of your results to see how the variables are related. You will make two graphs, one of volume versus pressure and another of the inverse of volume versus pressure. From your graphs you can derive the mathematical relationship between pressure and volume and verify Boyle's law.

OBJECTIVES

Determine the volume of a gas in a container under various pressures.

Graph pressure-volume data to discover how the variables are related.

Interpret graphs and verify Boyle's law.

MATERIALS

• Boyle's law apparatus or Vernier Gas Pressure Sensor and CBL setup

• carpet thread

• objects of equal mass (approximately 500 g each), 4

Always wear safety goggles and a lab apron to protect your eyes and clothing. If you get a chemical in your eyes, immediately flush the chemical out at the eyewash station while calling to your teacher. Know the locations of the emergency lab shower and the eyewash station and the procedures for using them.

Procedure

1. Adjust the piston head of the Boyle's law apparatus so that it reads between 30 and 35 cm^3. To adjust, pull the piston head all the way out of the syringe, insert a piece of carpet thread in the barrel, and position the piston head at the desired location, as shown in **Figure A** on the next page.
   Note: Depending upon the Boyle's law apparatus that you use, you may find the volume scale on the syringe abbreviated in cc or cm^3. Both abbreviations stand for cubic centimeter (1 cubic centimeter is equal to 1 mL).

2. While holding the piston in place, carefully remove the thread. Twist the piston several times to allow the head to overcome any frictional forces. Read the volume on the syringe barrel to the nearest 0.1 cm^3. Record this value in your **Data Table** as the initial volume (for zero weights).

Figure A

3. Place one of the weights on the piston. Give the piston several twists to overcome any frictional forces. When the piston comes to rest, read and record the volume to the nearest 0.1 cm^3.

4. Repeat step **3** for two, three, and four weights, and record your results in the **Data Table.**

5. Repeat steps **3** and **4** for at least two more trials. Record your results in the **Data Table.**

Data Table			
Pressure (number of weights)	**Trial 1 volume (cm³)**	**Trial 2 volume (cm³)**	**Trial 3 volume (cm³)**
0	33.0	33.0	33.0
1	29.7	29.5	29.0
2	26.8	26.8	26.0
3	24.3	24.1	23.5
4	22.0	21.8	21.2

DISPOSAL

6. Clean all apparatus and your lab station at the end of this experiment. Return equipment to its proper place.

Boyle's Law *continued*

Analysis

1. Organizing Data Calculate the average volume of the three trials for weights 0–4. Record your results in your **Calculations Table**.

0 weight: $\dfrac{33.0 \text{ cm}^3 + 33.0 \text{ cm}^3 + 33.0 \text{ cm}^3}{3} = 33.0 \text{ cm}^3$

1 weight: $\dfrac{29.7 \text{ cm}^3 + 29.5 \text{ cm}^3 + 29.0 \text{ cm}^3}{3} = 29.4 \text{ cm}^3$

2 weights: $\dfrac{26.8 \text{ cm}^3 + 26.8 \text{ cm}^3 + 26.0 \text{ cm}^3}{3} = 26.5 \text{ cm}^3$

3 weights: $\dfrac{24.3 \text{ cm}^3 + 24.1 \text{ cm}^3 + 23.5 \text{ cm}^3}{3} = 24.0 \text{ cm}^3$

4 weights: $\dfrac{22.0 \text{ cm}^3 + 21.8 \text{ cm}^3 + 21.2 \text{ cm}^3}{3} = 21.7 \text{ cm}^3$

2. Organizing Data Calculate the inverse for each of the average volumes. For example, if the average volume for three weights is 26.5 cm^3, then $\dfrac{1}{V} = \dfrac{1}{26.5 \text{ cm}^3} = \dfrac{0.0377}{\text{cm}^3}$. Record your results in your **Calculations Table**.

0 weight: $\dfrac{1}{33.0 \text{ cm}^3} = 3.03 \times 10^{-2}/\text{cm}^3$

1 weight: $\dfrac{1}{29.4 \text{ cm}^3} = 3.40 \times 10^{-2}/\text{cm}^3$

2 weights: $\dfrac{1}{26.5 \text{ cm}^3} = 3.77 \times 10^{-2}/\text{cm}^3$

3 weights: $\dfrac{1}{24.0 \text{ cm}^3} = 4.17 \times 10^{-2}/\text{cm}^3$

4 weights: $\dfrac{1}{21.7 \text{ cm}^3} = 4.61 \times 10^{-2}/\text{cm}^3$

Calculations Table		
Pressure (number of weights)	Average volume (cm^3)	1/Volume ($\times 10^{-2}/\text{cm}^3$)
0	33.0	3.03
1	29.4	3.40
2	26.5	3.77
3	24.0	4.17
4	21.7	4.61

| Boyle's Law *continued*

3. Analyzing Data Plot a graph of volume versus pressure on the grid below. Because the number of weights added to the piston is directly proportional to the pressure applied to the gas, you can use the number of weights to represent the pressure. Notice that pressure is plotted on the horizontal axis and volume is plotted on the vertical axis. Draw the smoothest curve that goes through most of the points.

Volume vs. Pressure

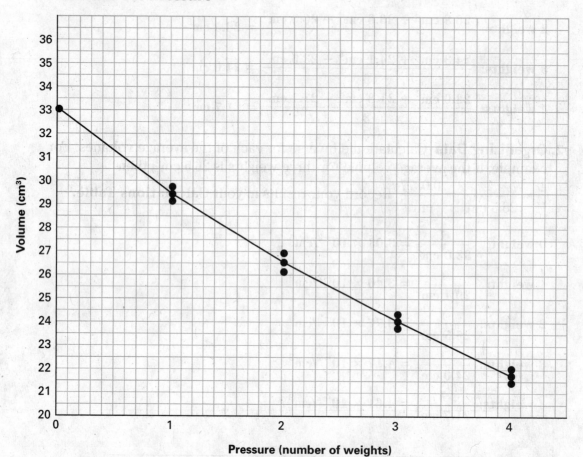

4. Interpreting Graphics Does your graph indicate that a change in volume is directly proportional to a change in pressure? Explain your answer.

No, the graph is not a straight line. Furthermore, as the pressure increases,

the volume decreases.

_____

_____

_____

| Boyle's Law continued

5. Analyzing Data On the grid below, plot a graph of $\dfrac{1}{volume}$ versus *pressure*.

Notice that *pressure* is on the horizontal axis and $\dfrac{1}{volume}$ is on the vertical

axis. Draw the best line that goes through the majority of the points.

$\dfrac{1}{\textbf{Volume}}$ **vs. Pressure**

6. Interpreting Graphics What do you conclude about the mathematical relationship between the pressure applied to a gas and its corresponding volume?
The graph of $\dfrac{1}{volume}$ **versus** *pressure* **is approximately a straight line (within**

experimental uncertainty). Therefore, $\dfrac{1}{volume}$ **must be proportional to**

pressure. **Pressure and volume are inversely related.**

Boyle's Law *continued*

Conclusions

1. **Applying Models** Correlate the observed relationship between the pressure and volume of a gas with the kinetic theory description of a gas.

   Gas pressure results from particles hitting the sides of the container. If the

   size of the container is decreased while the number of molecules remains the

   same, the number of hits increases.

2. **Applying Conclusions** Use your graph of $\dfrac{1}{Volume}$ vs. *Pressure* to predict the volume of the gas if 2.5 weights were used.

   Answers will vary.

   _____

3. **Analyzing Conclusions** If a normal sea-level recipe were used to prepare a cake at a location 1000 m below sea level, the cake would be much flatter than expected. Explain why, and offer a solution. (Hint: Consider how barometric pressure differs at this altitude and what effect that might have on the ability of the cake to rise.)

   At the lower altitude, the barometric pressure is greater. As a result, Boyle's

   law predicts that the gas bubbles will be smaller. To compensate for the

   reduced volume of gas, more baking powder or less flour can be added to the

   batter.

   _____

   _____

Molar Volume of a Gas

Teacher Notes

TIME REQUIRED 60 min

SKILLS ACQUIRED

Collecting data
Communicating
Experimenting
Identifying patterns
Inferring
Interpreting
Measuring
Organizing and analyzing data

RATING

Easy ◄—— 1   2   3   4 ——► Hard

Teacher preparation–2
Student Setup–2
Concept level–3
Cleanup–2

THE SCIENTIFIC METHOD

Make Observations Students observe the formation of hydrogen gas from a single-displacement reaction.

Analyze the Results Analysis questions 1 to 8 and Conclusions question 1

Draw Conclusions Conclusions questions 1 and 2

Communicate the Results Analysis questions 1 to 8

MATERIALS

To prepare 1.0 L of 6 M hydrochloric acid, observe the required safety precautions. Slowly and with stirring, add 516 mL of concentrated HCl to enough distilled water to make 1.0 L of solution.

After coiling the magnesium ribbon, tie the loops in a way that makes a compact magnesium mass.

In case of a spill, use a dampened cloth or paper towels to mop up the spill. Then rinse the towels in running water at the sink, wring them out until only damp, and put them in the trash. In the event of a spill of an acid, first dilute the spill with water and then proceed as described.

Measure the mass of 1.0 m of cleaned magnesium ribbon. This result is the second item in the **Data Table** on p. 63.

SAFETY CAUTIONS

Read all safety precautions, and discuss them with your students.

• Safety goggles and a lab apron must be worn at all times.

• Wear safety goggles, a face shield, impermeable gloves, and a lab apron when you prepare the HCl. Work in a hood known to be in operating condition and have another person stand by to call for help in case of an emergency. Be sure you are within a 30 s walk from a safety shower and an eyewash station known to be in operating condition.

• Procedure step **5** should be done by the teacher for each lab group. Students should not work with 6 M HCl. Wear safety goggles, face shield, lab apron, and gloves while dispensing the HCl into the student eudiometers. Students should stand clear and wear safety goggles and lab aprons.

TIPS AND TRICKS

Show students how to coil the magnesium ribbon and tie it onto the end of the thread.

Demonstrate how to place the eudiometer tube into the 400 mL beaker. (The HCl is too dilute to burn fingers in the time needed for inversion).

Trap some air in an eudiometer and demonstrate how the level of water inside the tube can change with respect to the level in the graduated cylinder as the tube is moved up and down in the cylinder. Show how the levels should look when you read the volume of the gas.

Discuss the reason why the piece of magnesium ribbon should not exceed 4.5 cm. Ask students if it should be shorter, or if it could be longer if they were working in a lab well above sea level.

If your school is located at high altitude, a shorter piece of magnesium ribbon should be used. The length of the piece can be determined either by trial and error or by reverse calculation.

Atmospheric pressure can be determined by contacting a weather service or using the Internet.

If atmospheric pressure is known in inches of mercury, use the conversion factor $\frac{25.4 \text{ mm}}{1.0 \text{ in.}}$ to convert to mm Hg.

DISPOSAL

Combine the used acidic solutions and add 1.0 M NaOH slowly and with stirring until the pH is between 5 and 9, then pour the solution down the drain. Residual magnesium should be rinsed with water, wrapped in newspaper, and put into the trash.

Name _____ Class _____ Date _____

Molar Volume of a Gas

Magnesium is an active metal that readily reacts with hydrochloric acid to produce hydrogen gas. In this experiment, you will react a known amount of magnesium, Mg, with hydrochloric acid, HCl, and collect and measure the volume of hydrogen gas, H_2, produced. From the volume of the gas measured at atmospheric pressure and the temperature of the lab, you can calculate the volume of the gas at standard temperature and pressure (STP). Knowing the mass of magnesium, you can calculate the number of moles of magnesium consumed and determine the volume of hydrogen at STP produced by the reaction of 1 mol of magnesium. This conclusion can then be related to the balanced equation for the reaction.

OBJECTIVES

Determine the volume of hydrogen produced by the reaction of a known mass of magnesium with hydrochloric acid.

Compute the volume of the gas at standard temperature and pressure.

Relate the volume of gas to the number of moles of magnesium reacted.

Infer the volume of one mole of gas at standard temperature and pressure.

MATERIALS

- 6 M HCl
- 50 mL beaker
- 50 mL eudiometer
- 400 mL beaker
- 1000 mL graduated cylinder or hydrometer jar

- buret clamp
- magnesium, Mg, ribbon (untarnished)
- ring stand
- rubber stopper, one-hole, #00
- thermometer, nonmercury, 0-100°C
- thread

Always wear safety goggles and a lab apron to protect your eyes and clothing. If you get a chemical in your eyes, immediately flush the chemical out at the eyewash station while calling to your teacher. Know the locations of the emergency lab shower and the eyewash station and the procedures for using them.

Do not touch any chemicals. If you get a chemical on your skin or clothing, wash the chemical off at the sink while calling to your teacher. Make sure you carefully read the labels and follow the precautions on all containers of chemicals that you use. If there are no precautions stated on the label, ask your teacher what precautions to follow. Do not taste any chemicals or items used in the laboratory. Never return leftover chemicals to their original containers; take only small amounts to avoid wasting supplies.

Call your teacher in the event of a spill. Spills should be cleaned up promptly, according to your teacher's directions.

| Molar Volume of a Gas *continued*

 Never put broken glass in a regular waste container. Broken glass should be disposed of separately according to your teacher's instructions.

Procedure

1. Fill a 400 mL beaker two-thirds full of water that has been adjusted to room temperature.

2. Measure about 4.4 cm of magnesium ribbon to the nearest 0.1 cm. Your piece of magnesium should not exceed 4.5 cm. Record the length of the ribbon in the **Data Table.**

3. Obtain the mass of 1 m of magnesium ribbon from your teacher and record this mass in the **Data Table.**

4. Roll the length of the magnesium ribbon into a loose coil. Tie it tightly with one end of a piece of thread approximately 25 cm in length. All the loops of the coil should be tied together as shown in **Figure A.**

5. This step requires the use of 6 M hydrochloric acid and will be performed by your teacher.
   CAUTION Hydrochloric acid is caustic and corrosive. Avoid contact with skin and eyes. Avoid breathing the vapor. Make certain that you are wearing safety goggles, a lab apron, and gloves when working with the acid. If any acid should splash on you, immediately flush the area with water and then report the incident to your teacher. If you should spill any acid on the counter top or floor, ask your teacher for cleanup instructions.
   Your teacher will carefully pour approximately 10 mL of 6 M HCl into a 50 mL beaker and then pour the 10 mL of HCl into your gas-measuring tube, or eudiometer.

6. While holding the eudiometer in a slightly tipped position, very slowly pour water from the 400 mL beaker into the eudiometer, being careful to layer the water over the acid so that they do not mix. Add enough water to fill the eudiometer to the brim.

7. Lower the magnesium coil into the water in the eudiometer tube to a depth of about 5 cm. Insert the rubber stopper into the eudio-meter to hold the thread in place, as shown in **Figure A.** The one-hole stopper should displace some water from the tube. This ensures that no air is left inside the tube.

Figure A

| **Molar Volume of a Gas** *continued*

8. Cover the hole of the stopper with your finger, and invert the eudiometer into the 400 mL beaker of water. Clamp the eudiometer tube into position on the ring stand, as shown in **Figure B.** The acid flows down the tube (why?) and reacts with the magnesium. Is the acid now more concentrated or dilute? Answer these questions and describe your observations in the place provided following the **Data Table.**

9. When the magnesium has disappeared entirely and the reaction has stopped, cover the stopper hole with a finger and carefully transfer the eudiometer tube to a 1000 mL graduated cylinder or other tall vessel that has been filled with water. Adjust the level of the eudiometer tube in the water as shown in **Figure C.** The levels of the liquid inside the eudiometer and the graduated cylinder should be the same. The hydrogen gas produced by the reaction will move to the top of the eudiometer. Read the volume of hydrogen gas you collected as accurately as possible.

10. Read the thermometer and record the temperature of the room and the hydrogen gas, H_2 in the **Data Table.** Determine the atmospheric pressure and record it in the **Data Table.**

11. Use the table of water vapor pressures in your textbook to find the vapor pressure of water at the temperature of the room. Record this water vapor pressure in the **Data Table.**

Figure B   **Figure C**

Disposal

12. Clean all apparatus and your lab station. Return equipment to its proper place. Dispose of chemicals and solutions in the containers designated by your teacher. Do not pour any chemicals down the drain or in the trash unless your teacher directs you to do so. Wash your hands thoroughly before you leave the lab and after all work is finished.

Data Table		
Length of Mg used	**4.2**	cm
Mass per meter of Mg	**0.981**	g/m
Volume of H_2 collected under lab conditions	**42.6**	mL
Temperature of H_2 collected	**20.0**	°C
Atmospheric pressure	**755**	mm Hg
Vapor pressure of water at observed temperature	**17.5**	mm Hg

Observations:

The acid flows down the eudiometer tube because it is denser than

water. The acid is being diluted. Gas bubbles begin to form and

rise to the top of the liquid. The magnesium ribbon starts to

disappear.

Analysis

For the following questions, show all your calculations in the space provided.

1. Organizing Data From the length of the magnesium ribbon you used and the mass of a meter of magnesium ribbon, determine the mass of the magnesium that reacted.

$$\text{Mass of Mg} = 4.2 \text{ cm} \times \frac{1 \text{ m}}{100 \text{ cm}} \times 0.981 \frac{\text{g}}{\text{m}} = 0.041 \text{ g}$$

2. Organizing Data Calculate the number of moles of magnesium that reacted. (The molar mass of Mg is 24.3 g/mol.)

$$\text{Moles of Mg} = 0.041 \text{ g} \times \frac{1 \text{ mol Mg}}{24.3 \text{ g}} = 0.0017 \text{ mol}$$

3. Organizing Data Because the hydrogen gas was collected over water, two gases were present in the eudiometer: hydrogen and water vapor. Calculate the partial pressure of the hydrogen gas you collected at the temperature of the room. (Hint: The sum of the two partial pressures equals atmospheric pressure.)

Pressure H_2 = 755 mm Hg − 17.5 mm Hg = 738 mm Hg

4. Organizing Data Calculate the volume of the dry hydrogen you collected at room temperature and standard pressure (760 mm Hg). (Hint: $P_1V_1 = P_2V_2$)

$$V_2 = \frac{P_1V_1}{P_2} = \frac{(738 \text{ mm Hg} \times 42.6 \text{ mL})}{760 \text{ mm Hg}} = 41.4 \text{ mL}$$

5. Organizing Data Calculate the volume of dry hydrogen gas at standard temperature (273 K). $\left(\text{Hint: } \dfrac{V_1}{T_1} = \dfrac{V_2}{T_2}\right)$

$$V_2 = \frac{V_1T_1}{T_2} = \frac{(41.4 \text{ mL} \times 273 \text{ K})}{293 \text{ K}} = 38.6 \text{ mL}$$

6. Relating Ideas Write a balanced equation for the reaction of magnesium with HCl. The products are hydrogen gas and $MgCl_2$.

$$Mg(s) + 2HCl(aq) \rightarrow MgCl_2(aq) + H_2(g)$$

7. Inferring Conclusions From the balanced equation, calculate the volume of dry hydrogen gas that would have been produced had you used 1 mol of magnesium at standard temperature and pressure.

$$\frac{\text{Volume } H_2}{1 \text{ mol Mg}} = \frac{38.6 \text{ mL}}{0.0017 \text{ mol Mg}} = 23\,000 \text{ mL/mol}$$

8. Analyzing Methods Why was it necessary to make a water vapor pressure correction of the atmospheric pressure in this experiment?

When a gas is collected over water, some of the water vaporizes and mixes

with the collected gas. To obtain the true pressure of the dry hydrogen, the

water vapor pressure must be subtracted from the total pressure.

_____

_____

_____

9. Analyzing Methods Why was it necessary to adjust the level of the eudiometer in the cylinder, as in **Figure C,** so that the level of water in the
eudiometer was the same as the level of water in the cylinder?

When the water levels inside and outside the eudiometer are equal, the

pressure of the gas inside the tube is equal to atmospheric pressure. If the

level of water in the eudiometer is below the level in the cylinder, the

pressure of the gas is greater than atmospheric pressure. If the level in the

eudiometer is above the level in the cylinder, the pressure of the is less than

atmospheric pressure.

_____

_____

_____

_____

Conclusions

1. Applying Conclusions From the balanced equation in Analysis question 6,
determine the volume of hydrogen gas at standard temperature and pressure
that can be produced from 3 mol of magnesium reacting with hydrochloric
acid.

Because there is a one-to-one mole ratio of Mg to H_2, 3 mol of magnesium

produce 3 mol of hydrogen gas. According to this experiment, at STP this is a

volume of 3 × 23 000 mL, or 69 000 mL.

_____

_____

Molar Volume of a Gas *continued*

2. **Applying Conclusions** Since the 1930s, alloys of aluminum and magnesium have been used in the manufacture of pots and pans. An unanswered question is whether a small amount of these metals that might dissolve in food as it cooks is beneficial, harmful, or of no consequence. What are some examples of foods that will react with aluminum/magnesium pans?

Acidic foods such as citrus fruits, rhubarb, sauerkraut, and pickles will react

with magnesium and aluminum.

_____

_____

_____

A Close Look at Soaps and Detergents

Teacher Notes
TIME REQUIRED 60 minutes

SKILLS ACQUIRED
Collecting data
Communicating
Experimenting
Identifying patterns
Inferring
Interpreting
Measuring
Organizing and analyzing data

RATING
Easy ◄——1——2——3——4——► Hard

Teacher Prep–3
Student Set-Up–3
Concept Level–3
Clean Up–2

THE SCIENTIFIC METHOD

Make Observations Students collect data on the properties of different kinds of soaps and detergents.

Analyze the Results Analysis questions 1 to 4

Draw Conclusions Analysis questions 1 and 2 and Conclusions questions 1 and 2

Communicate the Results Analysis questions 3 and 4 and Conclusions questions 1 and 2

MATERIALS

To prepare a bar-soap solution, add a single soap bar to 1 L of distilled water. Stir the solution occasionally, and allow the mixture to stand overnight. Remove the remainder of the bar. The mixture can be used directly. Alternatively, add 0.15 g of the soap bar to 10 mL of distilled water.

To prepare a liquid-soap or detergent solution, add 150 mL liquid soap (detergent) to 1 L distilled water. The mixture is a 1.5% (v/v) solution and can be used directly.

To prepare a solid detergent solution, mix 15 g of powdered detergent with 1 L of distilled water. The mixture is a 1.5% (w/v) solution and can be used directly.

To prepare a 4% $Ca(NO_3)_2$ solution, add 40 g of $Ca(NO_3)_2$ to 800 mL distilled water; stir until all the salt dissolves, and add distilled water to a final volume of 1 L.

To prepare a 0.5% alcoholic Sudan IV stain, add 0.5 g of Sudan IV (lipid and fat stain) to 10 mL of denatured isopropyl alcohol.

To prepare the colored fat sample, melt 4 to 5 tablespoons of lard in a double boiler. Once the lard is melted, add enough Sudan IV dye to obtain a dark pink or light red color. Solidify the fat by refrigerating it overnight. The dye will let students observe what happens to the fat as it is mixed with water and detergent.

Lard (hog fat) can be obtained from a grocery store; keep it refrigerated. Cut 2 in. squares of cotton fabric.

SAFETY CAUTIONS

Read all safety precautions and discuss them with your students. Include precautions on labels of commercially available products. In case of a spill, use a dampened cloth or paper towels to mop up the spill. Then rinse the cloth in running water at the sink, wring it out until it is only damp, and put it in the trash. Broken glass should be disposed of in a clearly labeled box lined with a plastic trash bag. When the box is full, close it, seal it with packaging tape, and set it next to the trash can for disposal.

Remind students of the following safety precautions:

- Always wear safety goggles and a lab apron to protect your eyes and clothing. If you get a chemical in your eyes, immediately flush the chemical out at the eyewash station while calling to your teacher. Know the location of the emergency lab shower and the eyewash stations and procedures for using them.

- Do not touch any chemicals. If you get a chemical on your skin or clothing, wash the chemical off at the sink while calling to your teacher. Make sure you carefully read the labels and follow the precautions on all containers of chemicals that you use. If there are no precautions stated on the label, ask your teacher what precautions you should follow. Do not taste any chemicals or items used in the laboratory. Never return leftovers to their original containers; take only small amounts to avoid wasting supplies.

- Call your teacher in the event of a spill. Spills should be cleaned up promptly, according to your teacher's directions.

- Never put broken glass in a regular waste container. Broken glass should be disposed of properly.

DISPOSAL

Unused solutions can be stored for reuse. Waste solutions can be washed down the drain.

TECHNIQUES TO DEMONSTRATE

Show students how to correctly measure the foam level. Emphasize that the measurement begins at the interface between the liquid and the foam.

TIPS AND TRICKS

Fabrics other than cotton may be used. You may wish to compare surfactant interaction with natural and synthetic fabrics.

Any detergent/soap solution can be used in **Part 1.**

Choose at least 5 representative soap and detergent brands in liquid, powder, and bar forms. Be sure to choose brands that list ingredients.

All soaps and detergents will foam in soft (distilled) water. Soaps, but not detergents, foam in 4% $Ca(NO_3)_2$.

Discuss emulsification of the fat by the soap or detergent sample. Students should understand that in **Part 3** the fat changes from a solid globular blob into tiny globules, eventually dispersing throughout the water.

Review the calculation of efficiency for this experiment.

Discuss why foaming is important to the cleansing action of surfactants.

Students should understand the relationship between the terms: *surfactant, soap*, and *synthetic detergent.*

Point out that liquid detergents are better because they contain a larger amount of nonionic surfactants than their dry counterparts. Liquid detergents are very effective at removing oily-type soils by emulsification. Anionic surfactants need help from other ingredients to prevent partial inactivation by water hardness ions.

Skills Practice

A Close Look at Soaps and Detergents

Soap is a surface-active agent (surfactant) that lowers the surface tension of water, allowing fat or oil-bearing soil particles to be suspended in water (emulsification). Although soaps are excellent cleansers in soft water, they are ineffective in hard-water conditions. Hard water contains aqueous salts of magnesium, calcium, and iron. When soap is used in hard water, the insoluble calcium salts of the fatty acids and other precipitates are deposited as curds. This precipitate is commonly referred to as bathtub ring or scale. To overcome this problem, inexpensive synthetic detergents were developed around 1950. Although immensely popular, these compounds were not biodegradable and were replaced in the mid-1960s.

Synthetic detergents, like soaps, have a long hydrocarbon chain labeled as a tail that is attached to a hydrophilic head. Synthetic surfactants are classified as anionic, cationic, or nonionic, depending on the type of hydrophilic head. The hydrophilic portion of a synthetic detergent is often a sulfonate, phosphate, or something other than the carboxyl group that is found in the soap. Therefore, synthetic surfactants are effective in both hard and soft water. No precipitates form when calcium, magnesium, or iron ions are present in solution. The most widely used group of synthetic detergents is the linear alkyl sulfonates (LAS). LAS are straight-chain compounds that have 10 or more carbon atoms and are easily degraded by bacteria.

Because water is a polar substance, it cannot remove dirt from fabrics if the dirt is suspended in oil and grease, which are nonpolar. The hydrocarbon tail of a detergent molecule dissolves itself in an oily substance but leaves the polar head outside the oily surface. Many detergent molecules continue to orient themselves in this way until the dirt containing oil is encapsulated. The oil droplet is then lifted away from the fabric and suspended in the water as a droplet or micelle.

OBJECTIVES

Observe the action of surfactants in reducing surface tension.

Evaluate the foaming capacity of commercial soaps and synthetic detergents.

Determine the efficiency of soaps and synthetic detergents in emulsifying a fat sample in water.

A Close Look at Soaps and Detergents *continued*

MATERIALS

- alcohol solution of Sudan IV, 0.5%
- balance
- beaker, 500 mL
- Ca(NO$_3$)$_2$ solution, 4%
- detergent (powdered and liquid)
- detergent solution, 1.5%
- Erlenmeyer flask, 125 mL (5)
- fabric, (two 2-in. squares)
- graduated cylinder, 100 mL
- hot plate

- lard
- medicine dropper
- metric ruler
- No. 5 solid rubber stoppers, 5
- soap (bar and liquid)
- stirring rod
- thermometer
- wax paper
- wax pencil

  Always wear safety goggles and a lab apron to protect your eyes and clothing. If you get a chemical in your eyes, immediately flush the chemical out at the eyewash station while calling to your teacher. Know the location of the emergency lab shower and eyewash station and the procedures for using them.

Do not touch any chemicals. If you get a chemical on your skin or clothing, wash the chemical off at the sink while calling to your teacher. Make sure you carefully read the labels and follow the precautions on all containers of chemicals that you use. If there are no precautions stated on the label, ask your teacher what precautions to follow. Do not taste any chemicals or items used in the laboratory. Never return leftovers to their original container; take only small amounts to avoid wasting supplies.

Call your teacher in the event of a spill. Spills should be cleaned up promptly, according to your teacher's directions.

Never put broken glass in a regular waste container. Broken glass should be disposed of separately according to your teacher's instructions.
   Never stir with a thermometer because the glass around the bulb is fragile and might break.

A Close Look at Soaps and Detergents *continued*

Procedure

PART 1–INVESTIGATING THE ACTION OF A SURFACE-ACTING AGENT (SURFACTANT)

1. Put on safety goggles, gloves, and lab apron.

2. Using a medicine dropper, carefully add single drops of distilled water to a square of clean fabric. Describe what occurs.

   <u>The water droplets bead up on the fabric's surface; very little water</u>

   <u>penetrates the fabric.</u>

   _____

   _____

3. Using a second medicine dropper, carefully add drops of detergent solution on top of the beaded water drops. Describe what happens.

   <u>The detergent reduced the surface tension and allowed the water to</u>

   <u>penetrate rapidly into the fabric.</u>

   _____

   _____

PART 2–EVALUATING CLEANSING CHARACTERISTICS OF SOAPS AND SYNTHETIC DETERGENTS

4. Use a wax pencil to label a set of five 5 Erlenmeyer flasks 1, 2, 3, 4, and 5.

5. Obtain five soap solutions from your teacher. Record in the **Table 1** the manufacturer's brand name next to each sample number. Then add 10 mL of each soap or detergent sample to its respective numbered flask.

6. Stopper flask 1 securely with a rubber stopper. Hold the flask with your thumb on the stopper, and shake it vigorously for 15 seconds. Allow the solution to stand for 30 seconds. Observe and measure the level of the foam. Record this value in the **Table 1**. Repeat this process for flasks 2 through 5. Which product has the highest foam level?

   <u>Answers will vary, depending on the brands tested.</u>

   _____

   _____

   _____

A Close Look at Soaps and Detergents *continued*

7. To each flask add 4 drops of 4% $Ca(NO_3)_2$ solution from a medicine dropper. Stopper the flask, and with your thumb on the stopper, shake vigorously for 15 seconds. Allow the solution to stand for 30 seconds. Observe and measure the level of foam. Record this value in the **Table 1.** Describe how $Ca(NO_3)_2$ affects a surfactant's ability to foam.

Ions from $Ca(NO_3)_2$ (hard-water conditions) inhibit the foaming action in

soaps. Calcium deposits (curds) or film deposits on the sides of the flask

may be observed with some soaps. Detergent foaming is unaffected by

hard-water conditions; precipitate deposition and film should not be noted.

PART 3–EVALUATING THE EFFECTIVENESS OF SOAPS AND SYNTHETIC DETERGENTS IN EMULSIFYING FAT

8. Fill a 500 mL beaker with 250 mL of distilled water. Set the beaker on a hot plate and heat the water to 55°C. Try to maintain this temperature as closely as possible throughout the experiment.

9. Measure a 0.1 g sample of colored fat onto a piece of wax paper.

10. Add the fat sample to the water in the beaker. Use a glass stirring rod to swirl the water and fat. Describe what happens.

The lard (fat) forms a distinct globular layer on the surface of the water.

11. Fill a graduated cylinder with exactly 100 mL of test sample 1.

12. While stirring constantly, slowly add sample 1 to the water/lard mixture until the fat is completely emulsified, as evidenced by the dispersion of the colored fat in water. Record in the **Table 1** the volume of detergent necessary to completely emulsify the lard (fat) globule. Clean the beaker and the graduated cylinder. Repeat steps 8–12 for each of the remaining samples.

13. Identify each sample tested as either a detergent or a soap in the **Table 1.** Based upon emulsification data, which soap and synthetic detergent brand is the most effective emulsifier? Give reasons for your answer.

The most effective emulsifiers require the least number of mL to emulsify

the fat.

A Close Look at Soaps and Detergents *continued*

TABLE 1: COMPARING SOAP AND DETERGENT BRANDS

Sample number	Foam level in water (cm)	Foam level in 4% $Ca(NO_3)_2$ (cm)	Volume needed to emulsify 0.1 g of fat (mL)	Efficiency rating (g/mL)	Soap or detergent
1 Softsoap™	2.3	1.3	100+	0.001 estimated	soap
2 Dial™	1.7	1.1	100+	0.001 estimated	soap
3 Wisk™ Free and and Clear	1.2	1.2	100+	0.001 estimated	detergent
4 Arm & Hammer™ Heavy Duty	1.1	1.2	100+	0.001 estimated	detergent
5 Joy™ dishwashing liquid	2.0	1.2	60	0.0017	detergent
6 Cascade™ powder	0.1	0.1	52	0.0018	detergent

DISPOSAL

14. Clean all apparatus and your lab station. Return equipment to its proper place. Dispose of chemicals and solutions in the containers designated by your teacher. Do not pour any chemicals down the drain or put them in the trash unless your teacher directs you to do so. Wash your hands thoroughly after all work is finished and before you leave the lab.

Analysis

1. Organizing Data For each sample tested, calculate its relative efficiency as a dirt and grease remover by dividing the 0.1 g of fat emulsified by the volume in milliliters of detergent added to the fat/water mixture.

$$\frac{0.1 \text{ g lard (fat)}}{35 \text{ mL soap sample}} = 0.028 \text{ g fat/mL}$$

Name _____ Class _____ Date _____

A Close Look at Soaps and Detergents *continued*

2. **Organizing Data** Construct a bar graph comparing the efficiency of soaps and detergents in emulsifying fat. Place surfactant samples along the *x*-axis and the efficiency along the *y*-axis.

3. **Applying Conclusions** You are demonstrating the effect of hard water on sudsing. You have all the demonstration materials except a source of hard water. All that is available to you is milk or a roll of antacid tablets. Can the demonstration proceed? Justify your answer.

Yes. Milk contains Ca^{2+} ions. Certain antacids contain CaCO$_3$. As the

mixture is stirred, the fatty acids in the soapy solution are converted into

their insoluble calcium salts.

A Close Look at Soaps and Detergents *continued*

4. Analyzing Data and Inferring Conclusions According to entries in the **Table 1,** which would be more efficient at dirt removal: a liquid detergent or a solid detergent? Explain.

Liquid detergents; efficiency values, and possibly foam heights, should be

higher.

_____

_____

Conclusions

1. Inferring Conclusions Many product labels on detergents state that the product will not harm septic systems. Suggest a reason for this based on your foam data.

The product will not produce calcium curds that can add scale and plug

plumbing.

_____

2. Inferring Conclusions Visit your local grocer and look for a popular brand of colorless hand gel. Write down the ingredients and compare them with the ingredients in various shampoos. Summarize your conclusions.

Formulations (major ingredients) are almost identical.

_____

_____

_____

Household Indicators

Teacher Notes

TIME REQUIRED Two 45-minute lab periods (45 minutes for Parts 1 and 2 and 45 minutes for Part 3)

SKILLS ACQUIRED
Collecting data
Communicating
Experimenting
Identifying patterns
Inferring
Interpreting
Organizing and analyzing data

RATING

Easy ◄———— 1   2   3   4 ————► Hard

Teacher Prep–3
Student Set-Up–3
Concept Level–2
Clean Up–3

THE SCIENTIFIC METHOD

Make Observations Students create a pH color chart for a household acid-base indicator and determine the pH of common substances.

Analyze the Results Analysis questions 1, 2, and 4.

Draw Conclusions Conclusions question 1 and Analysis question 3.

Communicate the Results Analysis questions 1 to 3 and Conclusion question 1.

MATERIALS

Wear safety goggles, a face shield, impermeable gloves, and an apron when you prepare the HCl or acetic acid solutions. Work in a chemical fume hood known to be in operating condition, and have another person stand by to call for help in case of an emergency. Be sure you are within a 30 second walk from a safety shower and eyewash station known to be in good operating condition.

To prepare 1 L of 0.1 M HCl solution, observe the required safety precautions. While stirring, slowly add 8.3 mL of 12 M HCl to 500 mL of distilled water. Dilute to 1 L. Pour solution into dropper bottles for lab use.

To prepare 1 L of 0.1 M CH_3COOH solution, observe the required safety precautions. Add 5.8 mL of glacial acetic acid to 500 mL of distilled water. Dilute to 1 L. Pour the solution into dropper bottles for lab use.

To prepare 1 L of 0.1 M H_3BO_3 solution, observe the required safety precautions. Add 6.2 g of H_3BO_3 to 500 mL of distilled water. Dilute to 1 L. Pour the solution into dropper bottles for lab use.

To prepare 1 L of $NaHCO_3$ solution, observe the required safety precautions. Add 8.4 g of $NaHCO_3$ to 500 mL distilled water. Dilute to 1 L. Pour the solution into dropper bottles for lab use.

To prepare 1 L of 0.1% ammonia solution, observe the required safety precautions. Add 100 mL of household ammonia to 900 mL of distilled water. Pour the solution into dropper bottles for lab use.

To prepare 1 L of NaOH solution, observe the required safety precautions. Add 4 g of NaOH to 500 mL of distilled water. Dilute to 1 L. Pour the solution into dropper bottles for lab use.

Select at least 10 of the common household substances listed in **Table 2**. Make sure "squeezings" and "slices" are made fresh, at the start of the laboratory. pH readings can change due to oxidation.

SAFETY CAUTIONS

Read all safety precautions, and discuss them with your students.

Safety goggles and an apron must be worn at all times.

In case of an acid or a base spill, first dilute with water. Then mop up the spill with wet cloths or a wet cloth mop while wearing disposable plastic gloves. Designate separate cloths or mops for acid and base spills.

Remind students of the following safety precautions:

• Always wear safety goggles and a lab apron to protect your eyes and clothing. If you get a chemical in your eyes, immediately flush the chemical out at the eyewash station while calling to your teacher. Know the location of the emergency lab shower and the eyewash stations and procedures for using them.

• Do not touch any chemicals. If you get a chemical on your skin or clothing, wash the chemical off at the sink while calling to your teacher. Make sure you carefully read the labels and follow the precautions on all containers of chemicals that you use. If there are no precautions stated on the label, ask your teacher what precautions you should follow. Do not taste any chemicals or items used in the laboratory. Never return leftovers to their original containers; take only small amounts to avoid wasting supplies.

• Call your teacher in the event of a spill. Spills should be cleaned up promptly, according to your teacher's directions.

• Never put broken glass in a regular waste container. Broken glass should be disposed of properly.

• Do not heat glassware that is broken, chipped or cracked. Use tongs or a mitt to handle heated glassware and other equipment because hot glassware does not always look hot.

DISPOSAL

Have students discard boiled cabbage leaves in a plastic bag that can be tied, labeled "Not for Consumption," and disposed of with the trash. Unused solutions can be stored for later use. Used solutions can be poured down the drain with lots of water.

TIPS AND TRICKS

Set up a clothesline so that students can dry their filter paper circles. Penciled initials allow students to identify their papers.

Use white well plates. Dark plates will not show the color changes.

Remind students that accuracy is relative; bias is introduced by the scientist's interpretation of the indicator charts.

Emphasize that accuracy and consistency go hand-in-hand. Caution students to take special care to avoid mislabeling.

Name _____ Class _____ Date _____

Household Indicators

A visual indicator is a chemical substance that reflects the nature of the chemical system in which it is placed by changing color. Most visual indicators are complex organic molecules that exist in multiple colored forms, one of which could be colorless, depending on the chemical environment. Many visual indicators are used to test a solution's acidity.

Acid-base indicators respond to hydronium ion concentrations, $[H_3O^+]$. Acidic solutions have an excess of H_3O^+ ions, while basic or alkaline solutions have few H_3O^+ ions. A measure of the $[H_3O^+]$ is pH. Chemists use p to mean "power," so pH means the power of the hydronium ions. Formally, pH is defined as the negative logarithm of the $[H_3O^+]$ of a solution.

The most common acid-base indicator is litmus, a blue coloring matter extracted from various species of lichens. The chief component of litmus is azolitmin. Widely distributed among the higher plants, anthocyanins constitute most of the yellow, red, and blue colors in flowers and fruits. Anthocyanins are excellent acid-base indicators because they exhibit color changes over a wide range of pH values. Red cabbage is a ready source of this pigment. Unlike litmus and anthocyanins, universal indicator is a mixture of various synthetic indicator molecules. Universal indicator provides pH scale coverage from 1 to 14 pH units.

In this investigation, you will extract the pigment from red-cabbage leaves and use it to prepare strips of pH indicator paper. You will use these paper strips to test the pH of common household materials. Then you will compare your results with pH tests made with litmus and universal pH paper.

OBJECTIVES

Extract anthocyanins from red cabbage leaves.

Prepare a pH indicator paper with the red cabbage anthocyanins.

Construct a color indicator chart for anthocyanins from red cabbage.

Compare and evaluate the accuracy of indicator papers for recording pH values of common items.

Household Indicators *continued*

MATERIALS

- 6-well spot plate, white
- beaker, 250 mL (2)
- CH_3COOH, 0.1 M
- clothespins
- colored pencils (red, rose, purple, blue, green, yellow)
- dropper bottles for acid solutions
- filter paper, 9 cm diameter
- fine-point scissors
- forceps
- H_3BO_3, 0.1 M
- HCl, 0.1 M
- hot mitt or pot holder
- hot plate
- household ammonia, 0.1%

- household materials: ammonia, apple, distilled water, fresh egg, grapefruit, fruit jelly, ginger ale, lemon, milk, milk of magnesia, molasses, orange, mineral water, sauerkraut, sweet potato, tomato, salt water, and tap water
- litmus paper, neutral
- medicine dropper
- metric ruler
- $NaHCO_3$, 0.1 M
- NaOH, 0.1 M
- red cabbage
- string
- universal pH paper, (1–14 pH units)
- wax pencil

 Always wear safety goggles, gloves, and a lab apron to protect your eyes and clothing. If you get a chemical in your eyes, immediately flush the chemical out at the eyewash station while calling to your teacher. Know the location of the emergency lab shower and eyewash station and the procedures for using them.

Do not touch any chemicals. If you get a chemical on your skin or clothing, wash the chemical off at the sink while calling to your teacher. Make sure you carefully read the labels and follow the precautions on all containers of chemicals that you use. If there are no precautions stated on the label, ask your teacher what precautions to follow. Do not taste any chemicals or items used in the laboratory. Never return leftovers to their original container; take only small amounts to avoid wasting supplies.

Call your teacher in the event of a spill. Spills should be cleaned up promptly, according to your teacher's directions.

Acids and bases are corrosive. If an acid or base spills onto your skin or clothing, wash the area immediately with running water. Call your teacher in the event of an acid spill. Acid or base spills should be cleaned up promptly.

 Never put broken glass in a regular waste container. Broken glass should be disposed of separately according to your teacher's instructions.

Household Indicators *continued*

🔥 **Do not heat glassware that is broken, chipped, or cracked.** Use tongs or a hot mitt to handle heated glassware and other equipment because hot glassware does not always look hot.

Procedure

PART 1–EXTRACTING ANTHOCYANINS FROM RED CABBAGE

1. Put on safety goggles, gloves, and lab apron.

2. Choose a red-cabbage leaf that has a dark purple color. Tear the leaf into small pieces.

3. Fill a 250 mL beaker 2/3 full with the leaf pieces. Add enough distilled water to just cover the pieces of cabbage leaf. Place the beaker on a hot plate, and bring the water to a slow boil. Continue heating for 5 minutes. Then turn off the heat, and allow the mixture to cool for 10 to 15 minutes.

PART 2–DYEING INDICATOR STRIPS

4. Using a hot mitt, remove the beaker from the hot plate. Carefully decant the cooled purple liquid into a second 250 mL beaker. Dispose of the cabbage-leaf material as directed by your teacher.

5. Using a pencil, write your initials on six filter paper circles. Using forceps, submerge the filter paper into the beaker containing the cabbage extract. Make sure that the papers are thoroughly wet. Then, using forceps, remove the filter papers from the beaker and allow them to dry thoroughly.

6. After drying, use scissors to cut from the filter paper 30 individual strips, each measuring 1 cm × 6 cm.

PART 3–CONSTRUCTING A COLOR INDICATOR CHART FOR THE ANTHOCYANIN-DYED pH PAPER

7. Use a wax pencil to label six wells in a spot plate 1 to 6.

8. Following the table below, add 10 drops of each named acid or base solution to its labeled well.

1	2	3	4	5	6
0.1 M CH_3COOH	0.1% household ammonia	0.1 M H_3BO_3	0.1 M HCl	0.1 M $NaHCO_3$	0.1 M NaOH

9. Into each of the six wells, dip a separate strip of the indicator paper prepared in **Part 2.** Record the color in **Table 1.** Rinse off the well plates.

Household Indicators *continued*

TABLE 1: pH AND INDICATOR COLOR

pH	Substance	Indicator color
1.0	0.1 M hydrochloric acid, HCl	red
2.9	0.1 M acetic acid, CH_3COOH	rose
5.2	0.1 M boric acid, H_3BO_3	purple
8.4	0.1 M sodium bicarbonate, $NaHCO_3$	blue
11.1	0.1 M ammonia, NH_3	green
13.0	0.1 M sodium hydroxide, NaOH	yellow

10. Use colored pencils and the entries in **Table 1** to fill in the following color indicator chart.

pH color chart for anthocyanins extracted from red caggage

Red		Rose		Purple			Blue		Green			Yellow	
1	2	3	4	5	6	7	8	9	10	11	12	13	14

PART 4–COMPARING AND EVALUATING THE ACCURACY OF INDICATOR PAPERS

11. Test each item listed in **Table 2** with universal pH paper, litmus paper, and the anthocyanin paper prepared in **Part 2**. Test each of the liquids listed by placing 10 drops of the liquid in a spot-plate well. Test the juice of each solid. Record the pH values in **Table 2.**

12. Clean all apparatus and your lab station. Return equipment to its proper place. Dispose of chemicals and solutions in the containers designated by your teacher. Do not pour any chemicals down the drain or put them in the trash unless your teacher directs you to do so. Wash your hands thoroughly after all work is finished and before you leave the lab.

Name _____ Class _____ Date _____

Household Indicators *continued*

TABLE 2: pH OF COMMON SUBSTANCES

Common substance	Measured pH	pH (neutral litmus paper)	pH (anthocyanin dyed paper)	pH (universal pH paper)
Ginger ale	2.0–4.0	<7	3–4	4.0
Lemon slice (lemon juice)	2.2–2.4	<7	1–2	2.0
Apple cider	2.4–2.9	<7	3–4	2.0
Apple slice	2.9–3.3	<7	4–5	2.0
Grapefruit (cut)	3.0–3.3	<7	2–3	2.0
Jellies, fruit	3.0–3.3	<7	2–4	2.0
Orange slice	3.0–4.0	<7	1–2	2.0
Sauerkraut	3.4–3.6	<7	1–2	2.0
Tomato slice	4.1–4.4	<7	5–7	2–4
Molasses	5.0–5.4	<7	6–8	5.0
Sweet potato slice	5.3–5.6	<7	5–7	5.0
Mineral water	6.2–9.4	<7	5–7	5.0
Milk	6.4–6.8	<7	5–7	5–6
Tap water	6.5–8.0	>7	8–9	8–9
Distilled water (CO_2-free)	7.0	7	5–7	8–9
Fresh egg	7.6–8.0	>7	9–11	7.0
Salt water	8.0–8.4	>7	8–9	7–8
Milk of Magnesia	10.5	>7	10–12	10–11
Household ammonia	10.5–11.9	>7	9–10	10.0

Analysis

1. **Organizing Conclusions** Do all three pH test papers cover the entire pH scale range? Use your data to support your answer.

   No. Neutral litmus paper has a pH range of 4.5 (red) to 8.5 (blue). Universal

   pH paper and cabbage indicator papers have wider pH scale ranges—

   essentially 1–14.

Household Indicators *continued*

2. Analyzing Data Which pH test paper was the most accurate within its respective pH scale range? Explain your reasoning.

Answers will vary. The Universal pH test paper is the most accurate. Both

the cabbage indicator and litmus papers provide a general indication of pH.

_____

_____

3. Inferring Conclusions Suggest reasons for the variation in measured pH values.

Answers will vary but may include pH scale differences, complexity of

indicator molecules, concentration of the indicator in the test paper or of

the test substance on the paper, variation in color perception, or testing

technique.

_____

_____

4. Analyzing Data Use the pH of a fresh egg to determine the hydronium ion concentration for the egg.

Because the pH of a fresh egg is about 8, the $[H_3O^+]$ is 0.000 000 01 M.

_____

$pH = 8$
$-\log [H_3O^+] = 8$
$\log [H_3O^+] = -8$
$[H_3O^+] = -10^{-8}$
$= 0.000\ 000\ 01$

Household Indicators *continued*

Conclusions

1. Inferring Conclusions The pH of cow's milk is approximately 6.5. When milk spoils, we sometimes say it has gone sour because of the lemon-like taste it develops. From your knowledge of food pH chemistry, what is happening to the milk's pH?

Lemon has an acidic pH and a sour taste. As acidity increases, the pH drops,

so one can assume that the taste is due to an increase in acidity and a

decrease in pH. (This acidity comes from the formation of lactic acid by milk-

inhabiting bacteria, *Lactobacillus acidophilus*.)

_____

_____

_____

2. Designing Experiments The acid-base indicator, phenolphthalein, is also a mild laxative and can be the active ingredient in commercial chocolate-flavored laxatives. Phenolphthalein is not soluble in water, but it is soluble in rubbing alcohol (70% isopropyl alcohol). How would you evaluate its effectiveness as an indicator?

Answers will vary. First, the indicator has to be extracted in a small volume

of rubbing alcohol. Its color range should be evaluated in a method similar to

this experimental procedure. (Phenolphthalein is colorless to pH 8.5 and

pink to deep red above pH 9.)

_____

_____

_____

Titration with an Acid and a Base

Teacher Notes

TIME REQUIRED 60 min

SKILLS ACQUIRED
Collecting data
Communicating
Experimenting
Identifying patterns
Inferring
Interpreting
Organizing and analyzing data

RATING
Easy ◄——— 1   2   3   4 ———► Hard

Teacher Prep–3
Student Set-Up–3
Concept Level–3
Clean Up–2

THE SCIENTIFIC METHOD

Make Observations Students observe the color change at the end point of a titration.

Analyze the Results Analysis questions 1 to 9

Draw Conclusions Analysis question 7

Communicate the Results Analysis questions 1 to 7

MATERIALS

To prepare 1.0 L of 0.500 M hydrochloric acid, use a fresh bottle of reagent grade concentrated HCl, preferably one that shows the actual assay of HCl rather than an average assay. Observe the required safety precautions. Assuming that the concentrated HCl is 12 M, slowly and with stirring, add 41.65 mL to enough distilled water to make 1.00 L of solution. If a large number of students are to be provided with solutions, it's best to make up 10.0 L in a large dispenser to ensure the same concentration for all lab groups. However, it will be impossible to make the HCl exactly 0.500 M without the accuracy of a volumetric flask. Some 5 gal carboys with spigots make ideal dispensers for the acid and base solutions.

To prepare 1.0 L of 0.6 M sodium hydroxide solution, observe the required safety precautions. Stir while adding 24 g of NaOH to enough distilled water to make 1.0 L of solution.

To prepare 1.0 L of phenolphthalein solution, dissolve 10 g of phenolphthalein in 500 mL of denatured alcohol and add 500 mL of water.

A wet cloth mop can be rinsed out a few times and used until it falls apart.

Bromthymol blue may be used as an indicator and is the more appropriate indicator for the titration of a strong acid with a strong base. For the concentrations of acid and base used, phenolphthalein and bromothymol blue give the same molarity results.

SAFETY CAUTIONS

Read all safety precautions, and discuss them with your students.

- Safety goggles and a lab apron must be worn at all times.

- In case of an acid or base spill, first dilute with water. Then mop up the spill with wet cloths or a wet cloth mop while wearing disposable plastic gloves. Designate separate cloths or mops for acid and base spills.

- Wear safety goggles, a face shield, impermeable gloves, and a lab apron when you prepare the NaOH and HCl solutions. For preparing HCl, work in a hood known to be in operating condition, and have another person stand by to call for help in case of an emergency. Be sure you are within a 30 s walk from a safety shower and an eyewash station known to be in good operating condition.

TIPS AND TRICKS

Demonstrate all techniques needed for successful titration: cleaning the burets, reading the buret with the eye at the liquid level, reading the buret scale correctly, swirling the flask, manipulating the stopcock, washing down the sides of the flask, and evaluating the color of the indicator.

Discuss the role of the indicator and the meaning of the terms *end point* and *equivalence point*. Indicators change colors at diffferent pH values. It is important to chose an indicator that changes color at a pH which is close to the pH of the equivalence point of the titration. For this titration, phenolphthalein is a good indicator.

It may help students if you work through a set of sample titration data.

DISPOSAL

Set out three disposal containers for the students: one for unmixed acid solutions, one for unmixed base solutions, and one for partially neutralized substances and the contents of the waste beaker. To neutralize the acid and base, slowly combine the solutions while stirring. Adjust the pH of the final waste liquid with 1.0 M acid or base until the pH is between 5 and 9. Pour the neutralized liquid down the drain.

Skills Practice

Titration with an Acid and a Base

Titration is a process in which you determine the concentration of a solution by measuring what volume of that solution is needed to react completely with a standard solution of known volume and concentration. The process consists of the gradual addition of the standard solution to a measured quantity of the solution of unknown concentration until the number of moles of hydronium ion, H_3O^+, equals the number of moles of hydroxide ion, OH^-. The point at which equal numbers of moles of acid and base are present is known as the equivalence point. An indicator is used to signal when the equivalence point is reached. The chosen indicator must change color at or very near the equivalence point. The point at which an indicator changes color is called the end point of the titration. Phenolphthalein is an appropriate choice for this titration. In acidic solution, phenolphthalein is colorless, and in basic solution, it is pink.

At the equivalence point, the number of moles of acid equals the number of moles of base.

$$(1) \quad \text{moles of } H_3O^+ = \text{moles of } OH^-$$

By definition

$$(2) \quad molarity \text{ (mol/L)} = \frac{moles}{volume} \text{ (L)}$$

If you rearrange equation **2** in terms of moles, equation **3** is obtained.

$$(3) \quad moles = molarity \text{ (mol/L)} \times volume \text{ (L)}$$

When equations **1** and **3** are combined, you obtain the relationship that is the basis for this experiment, assuming a one-to-one mole ratio and the units of volume are the same for both the acid and base.

$$(4) \quad \text{molarity of acid} \times \text{volume of acid} = \text{molarity of base} \times \text{volume of base}$$

In this experiment, you will be given a standard hydrochloric acid, HCl, solution and told what its concentration is. You will carefully measure a volume of it and determine how much of the sodium hydroxide, NaOH, solution of unknown molarity is needed to neutralize the acid sample. Using the data you obtain and equation **4,** you can calculate the molarity of the NaOH solution.

OBJECTIVES

Use burets to accurately measure volumes of solution.

Recognize the end point of a titration.

Describe the procedure for performing an acid-base titration.

Determine the molarity of a base.

Titration with an Acid and a Base *continued*

MATERIALS

- 0.500 M HCl
- 50 mL burets, 2
- 100 mL beakers, 3
- 125 mL Erlenmeyer flask
- double buret clamp

- NaOH solution of unknown molarity
- phenolphthalein indicator
- ring stand
- wash bottle filled with deionized water

 Always wear safety goggles, gloves, and a lab apron to protect your eyes and clothing. If you get a chemical in your eyes, immediately flush the chemical out at the eyewash station while calling to your teacher. Know the locations of the emergency lab shower and eyewash station and the procedures for using them.

Do not touch any chemicals. If you get a chemical on your skin or clothing, wash the chemical off at the sink while calling to your teacher. Make sure you carefully read the labels and follow the precautions on all containers of chemicals that you use. If there are no precautions stated on the label, ask your teacher what precautions to follow. Do not taste any chemicals or items used in the laboratory. Never return leftovers to their original container; take only small amounts to avoid wasting supplies.

Call your teacher in the event of a spill. Spills should be cleaned up promptly, according to your teacher's directions.

Never put broken glass into a regular waste container. Broken glass should be disposed of properly.

Procedure

1. Set up the apparatus as shown in **Figure A.** Label the burets *NaOH* and *HCl.* Label two beakers *NaOH* and *HCl.* Place approximately 80 mL of the appropriate solution into each beaker.

2. Pour 5 mL of NaOH solution from the beaker into the NaOH buret. Rinse the walls of the buret thoroughly with this solution. Allow the solution to drain through the stopcock into another beaker and discard it. Rinse the buret two more times in this manner, using a new 5 mL portion of NaOH solution each time. Discard all rinse solutions.

0.00 mL

HCl buret

NaOH buret

Buret clamp

50.00 mL

Erlenmeyer flask

Ring stand

Figure A

| Titration with an Acid and a Base *continued*

3. Fill the buret with NaOH solution to above the zero mark. Withdraw enough solution to remove any air from the buret tip, and bring the liquid level down within the graduated region of the buret.

4. Repeat steps **2** and **3** with the HCl buret, using HCl solution to rinse and fill it.

5. For trial 1, record the initial reading of each buret, estimating to the nearest 0.01 mL, in the **Data Table.** For consistent results, have your eyes level with the top of the liquid each time you read the buret. Always read the scale at the bottom of the meniscus.

6. Draw off about 10 mL of HCl solution into an Erlenmeyer flask. Add some deionized water to the flask to increase the volume. Add one or two drops of phenolphthalein solution as an indicator.

7. Begin the titration by slowly adding NaOH from the buret to the Erlenmeyer flask while mixing the solution by swirling it, as shown in **Figure B.** Stop frequently, and wash down the inside surface of the flask, using your wash bottle.

Figure B

| Titration with an Acid and a Base *continued*

8. When the pink color of the solution begins to appear and linger at the point of contact with the base, add the base drop by drop, swirling the flask gently after each addition. When the last drop added causes the pink color to remain throughout the whole solution and the color does not disappear, stop the titration. A white sheet of paper under the Erlenmeyer flask makes it easier to detect the color change.

9. Add HCl solution dropwise just until the pink color disappears. Add NaOH again, dropwise, until the pink color remains. Go back and forth over the end point several times until one drop of the basic solution just brings out a faint pink color. Wash down the inside surface of the flask, and make dropwise addition of NaOH, if necessary, to reestablish the faint pink color. Read the burets to the nearest 0.01 mL, and record these final readings in the **Data Table.**

10. Discard the liquid in the flask, rinse the flask thoroughly with deionized water, and run a second and third trial.

11. Record the known concentration of the standard HCl solution in the **Data Table.**

DISPOSAL

12. Clean all apparatus and your lab station. Return equipment to its proper place. Dispose of chemicals and solutions in the containers designated by your teacher. Do not pour any chemicals down the drain or in the trash unless your teacher directs you to do so. Wash your hands thoroughly before you leave the lab and after all work is finished.

Data Table

	Buret readings (ml)			
	HCl		NaOH	
Trial	Initial	Final	Initial	Final
1	0.70	10.90	5.08	13.58
2	10.90	20.80	13.58	21.80
3	20.80	28.81	21.80	28.33

Molarity of HCl __0.500 M__

Analysis

1. **Organizing Data** Calculate the volumes of acid used in the three trials. Show your calculations and record your results below.

Trial 1: Volume of HCl = __10.90 mL − 0.70 mL = 10.20 mL__

Trial 2: Volume of HCl = __20.80 mL − 10.90 mL = 9.90 mL__

Trial 3: Volume of HCl = __28.81 mL − 20.80 mL = 8.01 mL__

| Titration with an Acid and a Base *continued*

2. Organizing Data Calculate the volumes of base used in the three trials. Show your calculations and record your results below.

Trial 1: Volume of NaOH = 13.58 mL − 5.08 mL = 8.50 mL

Trial 2: Volume of NaOH = 21.80 mL − 13.58 mL = 8.22 mL

Trial 3: Volume of NaOH = 28.33 mL − 21.80 mL = 6.53 mL

3. Organizing Data Use equation 3 in the introduction to determine the number of moles of acid used in each of the three trials. Show your calculations and record your results below.

Trial 1: Moles of acid = 0.500 M × 0.01020 L = 0.00510 mol

Trial 2: Moles of acid = 0.500 M × 0.00990 L = 0.00495 mol

Trial 3: Moles of acid = 0.500 M × 0.00801 L = 0.00401 mol

4. Relating Ideas Write the balanced equation for the reaction between HCl and NaOH.

$HCl + NaOH \rightarrow NaCl + H_2O$

5. Organizing Ideas Use the mole ratio in the balanced equation and the moles of acid from **Analysis** item **3** to determine the number of moles of base neutralized in each trial. Show your calculations and record your results below.

Trial 1: Moles of acid = 0.00510 mol = *moles of base*

Trial 2: Moles of acid = 0.00495 mol = *moles of base*

Trial 3: Moles of acid = 0.00401 mol = *moles of base*

6. Organizing Data Use equation 2 in the introduction and the results of **Analysis** item **2** and **5** to calculate the molarity of the base for each trial. Show your calculations and record your results below.

Trial 1: Molarity of NaOH $\dfrac{moles\ NaOH}{volume\ NaOH} = \dfrac{0.00510\ mol}{0.00850\ L} = 0.600\ M$

Trial 2: Molarity of NaOH $\dfrac{0.00495\ mol}{0.00850\ L} = 0.602\ M$

Trial 3: Molarity of NaOH $\dfrac{0.00401\ mol}{0.00653\ L} = 0.614\ M$

7. Organizing Conclusions Calculate the average molarity of the base. Show your calculations and record your result below.

Average molarity of NaOH = $\dfrac{0.600\ M + 0.602\ M + 0.614\ M}{3} = 0.605\ M$

Name _____ Class _____ Date _____

Conclusions

1. Analyzing Methods In step **6,** you added deionized water to the HCl solution in the Erlenmeyer flask before titrating. Why did the addition of the water not affect the results?

Diluting with water did not change the number of moles of HCl in the flask.

NaOH was added until the number of moles of NaOH equaled the number of

moles of HCl.

_____

_____

2. Analyzing Methods What characteristic of phenolphthalein made it appropriate to use in this titration? Could you have done the experiment without it? How does phenolphthalein's end point relate to the equivalence point of the reaction?

Phenolphthalein changes from colorless in acid solution to pink in basic

solution. Without an indicator such as phenolphthalein, there would have

been no visual way to determine when the equivalence point had been

reached. Phenolphthalein's end point is close to the equivalence point

(neutral pH) of this titration.

_____

_____

_____

Hydronium Ion Concentration and pH

Teacher Notes

TIME REQUIRED 60 min

SKILLS ACQUIRED
Collecting data
Communicating
Experimenting
Identifying patterns
Interpreting
Organizing and analyzing data
Predicting

RATING

Easy ◄——1———2———3———4——► Hard

Teacher Prep–3
Student Set-Up–3
Concept Level–3
Clean Up–3

THE SCIENTIFIC METHOD

Make Observations Students observe the effects of adding drops of various solutions to pH paper.

Analyze the Results Analysis questions 1 and 2

Draw Conclusions Analysis question 3 and Conclusions question 1

Communicate the Results Analysis questions 1 to 3 and Conclusion question 1

MATERIALS

Wear safety goggles, a face shield, impermeable gloves, and a lab apron when you prepare the NaOH, HCl, H_3PO_4, NH_3, and CH_3COOH solutions. For all except NaOH and H_3PO_4, work in a hood known to be in operating condition, with another person nearby to call for help in case of an emergency. Be sure you are within a 30 s walk from a safety shower and an eyewash station known to be in good operating condition.

To prepare 1.0 L of 0.033 M phosphoric acid, H_3PO_4, observe the required safety precautions. Slowly stir 2.0 mL of concentrated H_3PO_4 into enough deionized water to make 1.0 L of solution.

To prepare 1.0 L of 0.1 M acetic acid, CH_3COOH, observe the required safety precautions. Slowly stir 6.0 mL of glacial acetic acid into enough deionized water to make 1.0 L of solution.

To prepare 1.0 L of 0.1 M hydrochloric acid, HCl, observe the required safety precautions. Slowly stir 9.0 mL of concentrated HCl into enough deionized water to make 1.0 L of solution.

To prepare 1.0 L of 0.1 M sodium chloride, NaCl, dissolve 6.0 g of solid NaCl in enough deionized water to make 1.0 L of solution.

To prepare 1.0 L of 0.1 M sodium carbonate, Na_2CO_3, dissolve 5.0 g of solid Na_2CO_3 in enough deionized water to make 1.0 L of solution.

To prepare 1.0 L of 0.1 M sodium hydrogen carbonate, $NaHCO_3$, dissolve 8.0 g of solid $NaHCO_3$ in enough deionized water to make 1.0 L of solution.

To prepare 1.0 L of 0.1 M sodium hydroxide, NaOH, observe the required safety precautions. Slowly stir 4.0 g of solid NaOH in enough deionized water to make 1.0 L of solution.

To prepare 1.0 L of 0.1 M aqueous ammonia, NH_3, observe the required safety precautions. Slowly stir 7.0 mL of concentrated $NH_3(aq)$ into enough deionized water to make 1.0 L of solution.

To prepare 1.0 L of 0.1 M ammonium acetate, CH_3COONH_4, dissolve 8.0 g of solid CH_3COONH_4 in enough deionized water to make 1.0 L of solution.

Best results are obtained by using Panapeha brand pH strips. Each strip contains six squares for color matching and covers pH values of 1–14. Also available are EM brand pH strips, which contain four squares per strip. EM paper is available in wide and narrow range.

SAFETY CAUTIONS

Read all safety precautions, and discuss them with your students.

• Safety goggles and a lab apron must be worn at all times.

• In case of an acid or base spill, first dilute it with water. Then mop up the spill with wet cloths or a wet cloth mop while wearing disposable plastic gloves. Designate separate cloths or mops for acid and base spills.

DISPOSAL

Combine all solutions containing H_3PO_4 and adjust the pH to between 5 and 9 using 1.0 M potassium hydroxide, KOH. (Do not use sodium hydroxide, NaOH, because the EPA does not want sodium hydrogen phosphates in the water.) Then pour the adjusted solution down the drain. Combine all other solutions and adjust the pH to between 6 and 8, and pour the adjusted solution down the drain.

TIPS AND TRICKS

Show students how to test the solutions and compare the test paper with the pH wide-range and narrow-range standards. Caution them to avoid poor results by thoroughly cleaning and drying the stirring rod between tests.

Skills Practice

Hydronium Ion Concentration and pH

For pure water at 25°C, the hydronium ion concentration, $[H_3O^+]$, is 1.0×10^{-7} M or 10^{-7} M.

In *acidic* solutions, the hydronium ion concentration is *greater* than 1×10^{-7} M. For example, the H_3O^+ concentration of a 0.00 001 M hydrochloric acid (HCl) solution is 1×10^{-5} M.

In *basic* solutions, the hydronium ion concentration is *less* than 1×10^{-7} M. The hydronium ion concentration in a basic solution can be determined from the equation for K_w when the hydroxide ion concentration, $[OH^-]$, is known.

(1) $\qquad K_w = [H_3O^+][OH^-] = 1 \times 10^{-14}\ mol^2/L^2$

(2) $\qquad\qquad [H_3O^+] = \dfrac{1 \times 10^{-14}\ mol^2/L^2}{[OH^-]}$

Therefore, the concentration of H_3O^+ in a 0.000 01 M NaOH basic solution is

$$[H_3O^+] = \frac{1 \times 10^{-14}\ mol^2/L^2}{[OH^-]} = \frac{1 \times 10^{-14}\ mol^2/L^2}{0.000\ 01\ mol/L} = \frac{1 \times 10^{-14}\ mol^2/L^2}{1 \times 10^{-5}\ mol/L}$$

$$= 1 \times 10^{-9}\ mol/L$$

The pH of a solution is defined as the negative of the common logarithm of the hydronium ion concentration. Therefore, for a 1×10^{-5} M HCl solution,

(3) $\qquad pH = -\log [H_3O^+]$

$\qquad\qquad = -\log (1 \times 10^{-5}) = 5$

For a 1×10^{-5} M NaOH solution, from equation **2**,

$$[H_3O^+] = \frac{1 \times 10^{-14}\ mol^2/L^2}{1 \times 10^{-5}\ mol/L} = 1 \times 10^{-9}\ mol/L$$

$$\text{and } pH = -\log (1 \times 10^{-9}) = 9$$

Values for pH that are greater than 7 indicate a basic solution. The higher the pH above the value of 7, the stronger the base and the smaller the hydronium ion concentration.

OBJECTIVES

Use pH paper and standard colors to determine the pH of a solution.

Determine hydronium ion concentrations from experimental data.

Describe the effect of dilution on the pH of acids and sodium hydroxide.

Relate pH to the acidity and basicity of solutions.

Hydronium Ion Concentration and pH *continued*

MATERIALS

- 0.033 M H_3PO_4
- 0.10 M CH_3COOH
- 0.10 M HCl
- 0.10 M NaCl
- 0.10 M Na_2CO_3
- 0.10 M $NaHCO_3$
- 0.10 M NaOH
- 0.10 M NH_3, aqueous
- 0.10 M CH_3COONH_4

- 10 mL graduated cylinder
- 50 mL graduated cylinder
- 250 mL beaker
- deionized water
- glass plate
- glass stirring rod, 25 cm long
- pH papers, wide and narrow range
- test tubes 9
- white paper, small sheet
- test tube rack

  Always wear safety goggles and a lab apron to protect your eyes and clothing. If you get a chemical in your eyes, immediately flush the chemical out at the eyewash station while calling to your teacher. Know the locations of the emergency lab shower and the eyewash station and the procedures for using them.

Do not touch any chemicals. If you get a chemical on your skin or clothing, wash the chemical off at the sink while calling to your teacher. Make sure you carefully read the labels and follow the precautions on all containers of chemicals that you use. If there are no precautions stated on the label, ask your teacher what precautions you should follow. Do not taste any chemicals or items used in the laboratory. Never return leftovers to their original containers; take only small amounts to avoid wasting supplies.

Call your teacher in the event of a spill. Spills should be cleaned up promptly, according to your teacher's directions.

Never put broken glass in a regular waste container. Broken glass should be disposed of properly.

Hydronium Ion Concentration and pH *continued*

Procedure

1. Place the glass plate on the sheet of white paper. Place a strip of wide-range pH paper and a strip of narrow-range pH paper on the glass plate.

2. Obtain samples of all of the solutions listed in **Data Table 1.** To find the pH of each solution, dip a clean stirring rod into each solution and apply a drop of the solution first to the wide-range pH paper and then to the narrow-range pH paper. **Figure A** shows the correct technique. Compare the color produced by each solution with the colors on the charts included with the pH papers. Be sure to rinse and dry the stirring rod before you test each solution. Record your results in **Data Table 1.**

Stirring rod with drop of solution

pH paper strips

Glass plate

White paper

Figure A

3. Using the 10 mL graduated cylinder, measure 5.0 mL of 0.10 M HCl. Dilute it to 50 mL in the 50 mL graduated cylinder with deionized water added from the 10 mL graduated cylinder. Stir the solution with a stirring rod. Transfer 5.0 mL of the diluted solution to a labeled test tube. Using the 10 mL graduated cylinder, measure and save 5.0 mL of the diluted solution from the 50 mL graduated cylinder. Empty the 50 mL graduated cylinder into a waste container, and rinse it with deionized water.

4. Repeat step **3** two more times, starting with the 5.0 mL of *diluted* solution you just made and measured in the 10 mL graduated cylinder.

Data Table 1			
0.1 M solution	**pH**	**0.1 M solution**	**pH**
HCl	1	NaCl	7
CH_3COOH	3	Na_2CO_3	11
H_3PO_4	1.5	$NaHCO_3$	8
NaOH	13	CH_3COONH_4	7
NH_3	11		

5. Repeat steps **3** and **4** for 0.10 M NaOH and 0.10 M CH₃COOH. Record your
results for each test in **Data Table 2.**

DISPOSAL

6. Clean all apparatus and your lab station. Return equipment to its
proper place. Dispose of chemicals and solutions in the containers
designated by your teacher. Do not pour any chemicals down the drain
or in the trash unless your teacher directs you to do so. Wash your hands
thoroughly after all work is finished and before you leave the lab.

Data Table 2

Concentration (M)	HCl	NaOH	CH₃COOH
0.10		Students' answers will vary.	
0.010			
0.0010			
0.000 10			

Analysis

1. Organizing Data List the solutions in order of decreasing acid strength using
your results from step **2.**

HCl, H₃PO₄, CH₃COOH, CH₃COONH₄, NaCl, NaHCO₃, NH₃, Na₂CO₃, NaOH

_____

_____

_____

2. Organizing Data Calculate the theoretical pH values for the concentrations
prepared in steps **3–5.** Record these values below.

HCl	Calculated pH	NaOH	Calculated pH
0.10 M	1	0.10 M	13
0.010 M	2	0.010 M	12
0.0010 M	3	0.0010 M	11
0.000 10 M	4	0.000 10 M	10

3. Analyzing Results What effect does dilution have on the pH of (a) an acid and (b) a base?

a. The pH of an acid increases as the solution is made more dilute.

_____

b. The pH of a base decreases as the solution is made more dilute.

_____

Conclusions

1. Predicting Outcomes Solutions with a pH of 12 or greater dissolve hair. Would a cotton shirt or a wool shirt be affected by a spill of 0.1 M sodium hydroxide? Explain.

A shirt made from wool, which is animal hair, will dissolve in the sodium

hydroxide solution. This will happen because, according to the calculations

for question 2, 0.1 M NaOH has a pH of 13.

_____

_____

_____

_____

Interpretation, Conclusions and Discussion

3. Analyzing Results. Within...

They think back to your...

Conclusions

Predicting Outcomes. Solid solution...

Temperature of a Bunsen Burner Flame

Teacher Notes

TIME REQUIRED 25 min

SKILLS ACQUIRED

Collecting data
Communicating
Experimenting
Identifying patterns
Inferring
Interpreting
Organizing and analyzing data
Predicting

RATING

Easy ← 1 2 3 4 → Hard

Teacher Prep–1
Student Set-Up–1
Concept Level–3
Clean Up–1

THE SCIENTIFIC METHOD

Make Observations Students make observations of the degree to which various heated metals raise the temperature of water.

Analyze the Results Analysis questions 1 to 4, and 6 to 9

Draw Conclusions Conclusions questions 1 and 2 and Analysis question 5

Communicate the Results Analysis questions 1 to 9

MATERIALS

Large copper or iron nuts can be purchased from the hardware store.

SAFETY CAUTIONS

Read all safety precautions, and discuss them with your students.

• Safety goggles and a lab apron must be worn at all times.

• Immerse the hot metal in the water slowly to avoid spattering of hot water. Wipe up spatters with paper towels, wring them out at the sink until they are only damp, and put them in the trash.

DISPOSAL

Save the metal objects for future labs.

TIPS AND TRICKS

• Suggest ways to attach the Nichrome wire to the metal object.

• If students have difficulty with the equations in the introduction, it may help to go through the calculations with a set of sample data. Some students may be interested in making the correction for the evaporated water discussed in **Questions 2** and **3.** Suggest that they obtain the mass of the foam cup and water after the metal object is removed.

Temperature of a Bunsen Burner Flame

When a hot solid is immersed in a cool liquid, heat flows from the hot object to the cool liquid. In fact, the number of joules of energy lost by the hot solid (ΔQ_1) equals the number of joules of energy gained by the cool liquid (ΔQ_2).

$$-\Delta Q_1 = +\Delta Q_2$$

The quantity of energy that is lost or gained is a function of the object's mass and specific heat. Every material has a characteristic specific heat, C_p, which is the number of joules of energy needed to change the temperature of 1.0 g of material 1.0°C. Some specific heats are given in **Table 1.** If the mass, temperature change, and specific heat of a substance are known, the energy lost or gained can be calculated using this relationship: $\Delta Q = (mass)(specific\ heat)(\Delta T)$. The temperature change is defined as $\Delta T = T_{final} - T_{initial}$.

In this experiment, you will determine the temperature of a Bunsen burner flame by heating a sample of a known metal in the flame and then immersing the hot metal at temperature T_1 into a measured quantity of water at temperature T_2. As the energy flows from the hot metal to the cool water, the two materials approach an intermediate temperature T_3. These changes are shown graphically in **Figure A.**

$$-\Delta Q_1 = \Delta Q_2$$

$$-(m_1)(c_{p1})(T_3 - T_1) = (m_2)(c_{p2})(T_3 - T_2)$$

By solving the equation for T_1, you can find the initial temperature of the hot metal. The metal should be the same temperature as the Bunsen burner flame.

Figure A

OBJECTIVES

Observe the change in temperature of a known mass of water when a heated metal object of known mass is placed in it.

Use the specific heat of the metal and of water to calculate the initial temperature of the object.

Relate the temperature of the object to the temperature of the Bunsen burner flame.

MATERIALS

- balance
- Bunsen burner
- foam cup
- iron ring

- metal object (Fe or Cu), 20–30 g
- Nichrome wire, 20 cm
- ring stand
- thermometer, nonmercury

 Always wear safety goggles and a lab apron to provide protection for your eyes and clothing. If you get a chemical in your eyes, immediately flush the chemical out at the eyewash station while calling to your teacher. Know the locations of the emergency lab shower and the eyewash station and the procedures for using them.

When using a Bunsen burner, confine long hair and loose clothing. If your clothing catches on fire, **walk** to the emergency lab shower and use it to put out the fire. Do not heat glassware that is broken, chipped, or cracked. Use tongs or a hot mitt to handle heated glassware and other equipment because hot glassware does not look hot.

Never put broken glass in a regular waste container. Broken glass should be disposed of properly.

Procedure

CAUTION: Remember that the metal object will become very hot.

1. Obtain the mass of an empty foam cup to the nearest 0.01 g, and record the mass in the **Data Table.**

2. Fill the cup about two-thirds full with water. Obtain the mass of the cup and water and record it in the **Data Table.**

3. Read and record the temperature of the water to the nearest 0.1°C.

4. Obtain the mass of the metal object to the nearest 0.01 g and record it in the **Data Table.**

5. Use the Nichrome wire to attach the metal object to the iron ring clamped on the ring stand. The object should hang about 7 or 8 cm below the ring.

6. Adjust the Bunsen burner so that it produces a hot blue flame. Move the flame under the metal object, and heat it for about 5 min.

Foam cup

Metal object

Figure A

Temperature of a Bunsen Burner Flame *continued*

7. Turn off the Bunsen burner and move it aside. SLOWLY lift the foam cup containing the water so that the hot metal becomes immersed in the water, as shown in **Figure B.** Hold the cup in this position for 2 min, stir the water, and then read and record the temperature of the water in the **Data Table.**

Data Table		
Type of metal used	**Ni**	
Mass of metal	**24.62**	g
Specific heat of metal (from **Table 1**)	**0.470**	J/(g·°C)
Mass of empty foam cup	**15.62**	g
Mass of foam cup and water	**225.32**	g
Initial temperature of water	**22.5**	°C
Final temperature of water	**33.2**	°C

Table 1: Specific Heats of Materials	
Substance	**Specific heat, J/(g·°C)**
Copper	0.385
Iron	0.444
Manganese	0.481
Nickel	0.470
Platinum	0.131
Tungsten	0.134
Water	4.18

DISPOSAL

Follow your teacher's directions.

Analysis

1. Organizing Data Calculate the change in the temperature of the water.

$$\Delta T = 33.2°C - 22.5°C = 10.7°C$$

2. Organizing Data What is the mass of the water that was heated by the metal object?

mass of H_2O = 225.32 g − 15.62 g = 209.70 g

Temperature of a Bunsen Burner Flame *continued*

3. **Organizing Data** Calculate the energy gained by the water. (Hint: Refer to the introduction.)

mass $\times \Delta T \times c_p$ = *energy gained by the water*

209.70 g $\times$ 10.7°C $\times$ 4.18 J/(g · °C) = 9380 J

4. **Inferring Conclusions** Calculate the temperature of the hot metal object. (Hint: Refer to the introduction. The energy lost by the metal equals the energy gained by the water.)

-24.62 g $\times$ 0.470 J/(g°C) $\times$ (33.2°C $- T_1$) = 9380 J

T_1 = 844°C

5. **Inferring Conclusions** What is the temperature of the Bunsen burner flame?

844°C

6. **Analyzing Information** From the specific heats of metals listed in **Table 1**, which metal would raise the temperature of the water the most in this experiment? the least?

Manganese would raise the temperature the most; platinum, the least.

7. **Evaluating Methods** Error is present in every experiment. In this experiment, the small mass of water that was changed to steam when the hot sample was initially immersed in the water was neglected. Would this tend to make the calculated temperature lower or higher than the actual temperature of the flame. Explain your answer.

Lower. It takes energy to evaporate each gram of water. This is energy as heat

that is neglected in the experiment. Additionally, some spattering occurs, so

the mass of water changing temperature is less the the original mass.

8. **Designing Experiments** It takes about 2.26 kJ of energy to evaporate each gram of water. Suggest a way to include the evaporated water in your calculation. (Assuming no water is ejected when the metal is inserted into the water.)

Determine the mass of the foam cup and water after the metal object has

been removed. Subtract this mass from the mass of the foam cup and water

before the object was immersed, to find the mass of the missing water.

Multiply the missing mass by 2260 J/g, and add the result to the energy

gained by the water.

Temperature of a Bunsen Burner Flame *continued*

9. **Evaluating Methods** Another source of error is the small amount of hot Nichrome wire that was heated and immersed in the water along with the metal object. Would this tend to make the calculated temperature lower or higher than the actual temperature of the flame? Explain your answer.

Higher. Energy in the form of heat from the small piece of hot Nichrome wire

would increase the temperature of the water slightly.

Conclusions

1. **Predicting Outcomes** If 100 g of boiling water at 100°C is poured into a 100 g platinum beaker at 0°C, an intermediate temperature will result. Knowing that the specific heat of water is about 32 times greater than the specific heat of platinum, approximate the intermediate temperature.

97°C; for every 1.0°C lost by the water, the platinum gains 32.0°C.

2. **Applying Ideas** In the eighteenth century, clothes were pressed using the heat from a heavy piece of metal with a flat, smooth side. This solid metal "iron" had to be heated periodically on top of a wood- or coal-burning stove. Disregarding cost, explain which of the metals listed in **Table 1** would be the best to use for this purpose.

Manganese. The metal with the largest specific heat absorbs the most energy

from the stove and loses its energy the slowest.

Counting Calories

Teacher Notes

TIME REQUIRED 45 min

SKILLS ACQUIRED
Collecting data
Communicating
Experimenting
Identifying patterns
Inferring
Interpreting
Organizing and analyzing data
Predicting

RATING

Easy ← 1   2   3   4 → Hard

Teacher Prep–3
Student Set-Up–3
Concept Level–3
Clean Up–2

THE SCIENTIFIC METHOD

Make Observations Students collect data in order to calculate the energy released by the combustion of peanuts and walnuts.

Analyze the Results Analysis questions 1 to 3

Draw Conclusions Conclusions question 1 and Analysis question 4

Communicate the Results Analysis questions 1 to 3 and Conclusions question 1

MATERIALS

• The nut samples should be of similar mass. Both types of nuts should be raw or dry roasted, or roasted in oil, for a better comparison of energy released.

• A home temperature digital recording device is suitable. Lab digital recording devices, and CBLs and probes, are also acceptable.

SAFETY CAUTIONS

Read all safety precautions, and discuss them with your students.

• Safety goggles and an apron must be worn at all times.

• A beaker filled with water should be placed at each bench setup to extinguish any uncontrolled burning.

• Designate one student from each group to monitor the group's activities and call out unsafe conditions or react to extinguish any uncontrolled burning. This individual will also time cooling periods to prevent potential scalding.

• Caution students to handle the butane lighter with care.

- Some people are severely allergic to nuts. Before beginning the lab, find out if any of your students are allergic to peanuts or walnuts. Remind these students not to eat or touch the nuts, and to avoid inhaling dust or smoke from the nuts. Some students may wish to be excused from this lab.

- Caution students to be extremely careful when handling the cut tin can. Edges can be sharp enough to cause lacerations.

TIPS AND TRICKS

- Have students practice assembling and disassembling the calorimeter, to prevent accidents and to keep to a minimum the time lost after ignition and burning of the food source.

- Student-calculated averages in the **Data Table** will be 20% to 40% of the published caloric value: 600 Cal/100 g for oil-roasted peanuts and 702 Cal/100 g for oil-roasted walnuts.

- Review the methods of heat transfer, combustion reactions, and accuracy in measurement.

DISPOSAL

Retorts, pie pans, and holder assemblies can be stored for reuse. Charred remains of food can be thrown out with trash.

Skills Practice

Counting Calories

We expend energy in three ways—through exercise, through specific dynamic action (SDA), and through basal metabolism (BM). Exercise is the composite of all physical work we do with our bodies. SDA accounts for the energy consumed in digesting and metabolizing food. BM accounts for the energy needed to maintain key bodily functions that sustain life.

Food provides energy. Food chemicals are classified as fats and oils, carbohydrates, or proteins. Fats furnish 9 Calories (Cal) per gram, carbohydrates furnish 4 Cal per gram, and proteins 4 Cal per gram. The amount of energy each of these chemicals delivers to the body is independent of the kind of food or quantity of other macronutrients. A meal containing 10 g of fat, 15 g of carbohydrates, and 20 g of protein would deliver 230 Cal of energy: 90 Cal from fat, 60 Cal from carbohydrates, and 80 Cal from protein. In this experiment, you will construct a calorimeter and indirectly determine the caloric content of peanuts and walnuts by measuring the temperature change in a sample of water.

Note: The *C* in nutritional *Calorie* is capitalized. The nutritional Calorie is equal to 1000 calories, or 1 kilocalorie.

OBJECTIVES

Construct a calorimeter setup.

Determine the amount of energy, in Calories, in oil-roasted walnuts and peanuts.

Compare measured caloric data.

Determine which nut is a better source of energy.

MATERIALS

- peanut halves
- walnut halves
- heavy aluminum foil, 5 × 5 cm
- 250 mL beaker
- 100 mL graduated cylinder
- aluminum pie plate
- can opener
- balance
- cork stopper
- digital temperature recorder or nonmercury thermometer
- knife or single-edge razor blade
- butane lighter
- metal file
- metric ruler
- paper clip
- pot holder
- 16 oz tin can, opened and clean
- tin snips

Always wear safety goggles and a lab apron to provide protection for your eyes and clothing. If you get a chemical in your eyes, immediately flush the chemical out at the eyewash station while calling to your teacher. Know the locations of the emergency lab shower and the eyewash station and the procedures for using them.

| Counting Calories *continued*

 Do not touch any chemicals. If you get a chemical on your skin or clothing, wash the chemical off at the sink while calling to your teacher. Make sure you carefully read the labels and follow the precautions on all containers of chemicals that you use. If there are no precautions stated on the label, ask your teacher what precautions you should follow. Do not taste any chemicals or items used in the laboratory. Never return leftovers to their original containers; take only small amounts to avoid wasting supplies.

Call your teacher in the event of a spill. Spills should be cleaned up promptly, according to your teacher's directions.

Never put broken glass in a regular waste container. Broken glass should be disposed of properly.

Never stir with a thermometer, because the glass around the bulb is fragile and might break.

When using a flame, confine long hair and loose clothing. If your clothing catches on fire, WALK to the emergency lab shower, and use it to put out the fire. Do not heat glassware that is broken, chipped, or cracked. Use a hot mitt or pot holder to handle heated glassware and other equipment, because hot glassware does not look hot.

Procedure

Before beginning the lab, inform your teacher if you have an allergy to peanuts or walnuts.

1. Use **Figure A** to prepare the retort. Remove the label from the tin can. Use the can opener to punch four triangular openings in the unopened end (top) of the can and three openings in the side of the can, near the top. Use tin snips to cut a viewing hole in the side of the can, beginning at the can's open end: 5 cm high, 3 cm wide at the top, and 4 cm wide at the bottom. Use a metal file to remove all burrs and sharp edges.

Figure A

Counting Calories *continued*

2. Refer to **Figure B** to construct the sample holder. Bend a paper clip so that it can hold food samples between the wires. Measure and cut the cork stopper so that its height, when resting on its widest flat surface, is 2 cm. Mold a piece of aluminum foil around the cork. Insert the bent paper clip into the cork. The total height of the holder assembly should be no higher than 3.5 to 4.0 cm.

1.5 to 2 cm

2 cm

Cork with base trimmed to 2 cm

Aluminum foil

Figure B

3. Obtain three peanut halves and three walnut halves to use as your six samples. Use a balance to determine the mass of each sample to the nearest 0.1 g. For each sample, record the type of nut and its mass in the **Data Table.**

4. Using a graduated cylinder, pour 100 mL of tap water into the 250 mL beaker.

5. Insert the temperature recorder into the beaker. Make sure that the sensing element is fully submerged and does not make contact with the bottom glass. If a digital temperature recorder is unavailable, use a nonmercury thermometer.

6. Measure the temperature of the water in the beaker; record this value in the **Data Table.**

7. Place a sample in the wire of your sample holder. Position the sample holder in the center of the aluminum pie plate.

8. Using a butane lighter, carefully set fire to the nut. Once burning is sustained, carefully position the retort (metal can with holes) over the burning sample so that the viewing hole faces you. Set the water-filled beaker on top of the retort. Refer to **Figure C.**

9. Carefully stir the water and observe the digital readout of the temperature until it starts to fall. Record the maximum temperature value in the **Data Table.**

Beaker with water

Retort

Aluminum plate

10. Cool the materials for 2 to 5 min. Using a pot holder, remove the beaker from the retort and pour the water into the sink. Using a pot holder, remove the retort from the pie plate.

11. Repeat steps **4** through **9** until you have collected data for three peanut halves and three walnut halves.

Sample holder

Figure C

| Counting Calories *continued*

DISPOSAL

12. Clean all apparatus and your lab station. Return equipment to its proper place. Dispose of chemicals and solutions in the containers designated by your teacher. Do not pour any chemicals down the drain or put them in the trash unless your teacher directs you to do so. Wash your hands thoroughly after all work is finished and before you leave the lab.

Data Table

| | Mass of sample (g) | Water temperature (°C) | | | Food energy | | |
		Before burning (T_1)	After burning (T_2)	Change in water temperature	calories	kcal	kcal per 100 g of food sample
Trial 1 peanut	0.60	21.9	30.0	8.1	810	0.810	
Trial 2 peanut	0.50	29.9	35.2	5.3	530	0.530	
Trial 3 peanut	0.60	22.0	30.0	8.0	800	0.800	
Average	0.57			7.1	710	0.710	120
Trial 1 walnut	1.5	26.8	52.7	25.7	2570	2.570	
Trial 2 walnut	2.0	22.0	57.0	35.0	3500	3.500	
Trial 3 walnut	1.4	21.0	46.8	25.8	2580	2.580	
Average	1.6			28.8	2880	2.880	180

Analysis

1. Organizing Data Determine the average mass for each nut type tested; record each value in the **Data Table.**

Answers will vary. Check that calculations are done correctly. Example data:

Peanuts: $\dfrac{0.60 \text{ g} + 0.50 \text{ g} + 0.60 \text{ g}}{3} = 0.57 \text{ g}$

Walnuts: $\dfrac{1.5 \text{ g} + 2.0 \text{ g} + 1.4 \text{ g}}{3} = 1.6 \text{ g}$

2. **Organizing Data** Calculate the change in water temperature for each trial in the **Data Table** by subtracting T_1 from T_2. Enter the results in the **Data Table.** Then calculate the average change in water temperature for each nut type tested; record the values in the **Data Table.**

Example data for peanuts:

For Trial 3, $T_2 = 30.0°C$ and $T_1 = 22.0°C$, so $T_2 - T_1 = 8.0°C$

Average temperature range $= \dfrac{8.1°C + 5.3°C + 8.0°C}{3} = 7.1°C$

3. **Organizing Data** Determine the number of Calories (kcal) contained in 100 g of food sample for both nut types tested; record the values in the **Data Table.** The energy transferred by the combustion of the nut equals the energy absorbed by the water. Use 1 cal/(g·°C) as the specific heat capacity of water when you calculate the number of calories.

Example data for peanuts:

$\Delta T = 7.1°C$ (from Data Table)

Since 100 mL H_2O = 100 g H_2O, and 1 cal = 1 g H_2O heated by 1°C,

$7.1°C \times 100$ g $H_2O = 710$ cal

710 cal $\times \dfrac{1 \text{ kcal}}{1000 \text{ cal}} = 0.710$ kcal

For an average mass of 0.57 g

$\dfrac{0.710 \text{ kcal}}{0.57 \text{ g}} = \dfrac{1.2 \text{ kcal}}{\text{g}}$

$\dfrac{1.2 \text{ kcal}}{\text{g}} \times \dfrac{100}{100} = \dfrac{120 \text{ kcal}}{100 \text{ g}}$

4. **Predicting Outcomes** Suppose a package of lunch meat contains 5% fat according to the label. This means that 5% of the mass is fat. What percentage of the total calories does this amount of fat provide? Assume that the lunch meat has a mass of 100 g and is 5% fat by mass.

The lunch meat sample contains 5 g of fat and 95 g of carbohydrates and proteins combined. Both carbohydrates and proteins have a caloric value of 4 Cal/g.

Calories from fat: $5 \text{ g} \times 9 \text{ Cal/g} = 45 \text{ Cal}$

Calories from carbohydrates and proteins:
  $95 \text{ g} \times 4 \text{ Cal/g} = 380 \text{ Cal}$

Total Calories = 45 Cal + 380 Cal = 425 Cal

Percentage of total calories provided by fat:

$\dfrac{45 \text{ Cal}}{425 \text{ Cal}} \times 100 = 10.6\%$

Counting Calories *continued*

Conclusion

1. **Inferring Conclusions** According to your experimental data, which of the nuts that you tested is a better source of energy? Why?

   Walnuts are a better source of energy because their caloric value is higher.

   However, if the peanuts have been roasted in oil and the walnuts are raw, the

   peanuts may yield more energy per gram.

Radioactivity

Teacher Notes

TIME REQUIRED One 45-minute lab period

SKILLS ACQUIRED
Collecting data
Communicating
Inferring
Interpreting
Organizing and analyzing data

RATING

Easy ←——1———2———3———4——→ Hard

Teacher Prep–2
Student Set-Up–2
Concept Level–2
Clean Up–2

THE SCIENTIFIC METHOD

Make Observations Students collect data on the properties of beta particles.

Analyze the Results Analysis questions 1 to 3 and Conclusions question 1

Draw Conclusions Conclusions questions 1 and 2

Communicate the Results Analysis questions 1–3 and Conclusions question 1

MATERIALS

Thallium 204 is an inexpensive beta source with a useful life of about 15 years. Read the special precautions about radioactive sources.

A decade scaler is an ideal radioactive counter. Thorton has an excellent scaler that is one of the least-expensive models available.

SAFETY CAUTIONS

Before your students perform this experiment, you should read the manufacturer's precautions for the use of the counter equipment. Be sure you and your students understand and follow all the precautions. Similarly, be sure you and your students will follow the supplier's precautions for the use and handling of the beta source. When not in use, the beta source should be kept secure in a locked location not accessible to students.

Read all safety cautions and discuss them with your students.

• Always wear safety goggles and a lab apron to protect your eyes and clothing. If you get a chemical in your eyes, immediately flush the chemical out at the eyewash station while calling to your teacher. Know the location of the emergency lab shower and the eyewash stations and procedures for using them.

- Do not touch any chemicals. If you get a chemical on your skin or clothing, wash the chemical off at the sink while calling to your teacher. Make sure you carefully read the labels and follow the precautions on all containers of chemicals that you use. If there are no precautions stated on the label, ask your teacher what precautions you should follow. Do not taste any chemicals or items used in the laboratory. Never return leftovers to their original containers; take only small amounts to avoid wasting supplies.

- Call your teacher in the event of a spill. Spills should be cleaned up promptly, according to your teacher's directions.

- Never put broken glass in a regular waste container. Broken glass should be disposed of properly.

DISPOSAL

Students must return the beta emitter to you for safe storage as described under Safety Cautions.

TECHNIQUES TO DEMONSTRATE

Be sure that students understand how to use the counter according to the directions accompanying your counters. Show students how to set up the counter and Beta source for measurement. Require that they measure the distances to ± 1 cm.

TIPS AND TRICKS

Ask students why it is necessary to determine a background count and subtract it from the values they obtain when measuring the output of the Beta emitter.

Discuss the graphing of data and what the slope of a straight line means when assessing the dependence of one variable on another.

Skills Practice

Radioactivity

aThe types of radiation emitted by radioactive materials include alpha particles, beta particles, and gamma rays. Alpha particles are helium nuclei; beta particles are high-speed electrons; and gamma rays are extremely high-frequency photons. Alpha particles will discharge an electroscope, but their penetrating power is not great enough to affect a Geiger counter tube. A few centimeters of air will stop an alpha particle. Beta particles can be detected by a Geiger counter tube and can penetrate several centimeters of air, but several layers of paper or aluminum foil can stop them. Gamma rays can penetrate through several centimeters of concrete.

The environment contains a small amount of natural radiation, which can be detected by a Geiger counter. This is called background radiation and is primarily due to cosmic rays from stars. A small amount of background radiation may also come from the walls of buildings made of stone, clay, and some kinds of bricks, and from other sources such as dust particles.

OBJECTIVES

Use a Geiger counter to determine the level of background radiation.

Compare counts per minute for a beta source passing through air, index cards, and aluminum.

Graph data and determine the relationship between counts per minute and thickness of material.

Graph data and determine the effect of distance on counts per minute in air.

MATERIALS

- aluminum foil
- index cards
- radioactivity demonstrator (scaler)
- thallium 204 (beta source)

 Always wear safety goggles and a lab apron to protect your eyes and clothing. If you get a chemical in your eyes, immediately flush the chemical out at the eyewash station while calling to your teacher. Know the location of the emergency lab shower and eyewash station and the procedures for using them.

Do not touch any chemicals. If you get a chemical on your skin or clothing, wash the chemical off at the sink while calling to your teacher. Make sure you carefully read the labels and follow the precautions on all containers of chemicals that you use. If there are no precautions stated on the label, ask your teacher what precautions to follow. Do not taste any chemicals or items used in the laboratory. Never return leftovers to their original container; take only small amounts to avoid wasting supplies.

Procedure

PART–BACKGROUND COUNT

CAUTION The wiring between the Geiger counter probe and the counter carries more than 1000 volts. Do not touch it when the equipment is operating or for at least 5 min after it has been unplugged from the electric socket.

1. Put on safety goggles, gloves, and lab apron.

2. Carefully read the directions on the operation of your counter. Set the counter to zero. Do not have any radioactive sources within 1 m of the Geiger counter tube. Turn on the counter for 1 min and count the frequency of clicks. Record the number of clicks per minute in **Table 1.** Repeat two more trials. The average of these trials will be your background count in counts per minute (cpm).

PART–RANGE OF BETA PARTICLES IN VARIOUS MEDIA

3. Air: Place the beta source approximately 5 cm from the Geiger tube. The proper setup is shown in **Figure 1.**
   CAUTION You should never directly handle a radioactive source. Be certain you are wearing gloves when handling the beta source (thallium 204).

   Determine the count for 1 min, and record your count/per minute and distance between the source and Geiger tube in **Table 2.**

4. Move the source another 5 cm, and determine and record the count for 1 min. Continue this procedure until you reach the background count or have completed 10 trials.

Figure 1

Geiger counter probe

Beta source

DIGITAL GEIGER COUNTER

| **Radioactivity** *continued* |

5. Paper: Place the beta source approximately 5 cm from the Geiger tube. Place a single index card on top of the beta source and determine the count for 1 min. Record the number of counts per minute in **Table 3.**

6. Keep the distance from the source to the Geiger tube constant, and repeat step **4** with an additional index card. Continue adding index cards and measuring and recording counts until the background count is reached or 10 trials have been completed.

7. Aluminum: Repeat steps **4** and **5,** but use sheets of aluminum foil in place of index cards. Record your data in **Table 3.**

8. Return the beta source to your teacher.

TABLE 1 BACKGROUND COUNT DATA

Background Count	
Trial	**Count/min**
1	data will vary
2	data will vary
3	data will vary
Average	data will vary

TABLE 2 RANGE OF BETA PARTICLES IN AIR

Air					
Distance (cm)	**Count/ min**	**Distance (cm)**	**Count/ min**	**Distance (cm)**	**Count/ min**

TABLE 3 PENETRATING POWER OF BETA PARTICLES

Index Cards		Aluminum	
No. Sheets	Count/min	No. Sheets	Count/min
0		0	
1		1	
2		2	
3		3	
4		4	
5		5	
6		6	
7		7	
8		8	
9		9	
10		10	

Analysis

1. **Organizing Data** On a separate piece of graph paper, plot a graph of counts per minute versus distance between the beta source and the Geiger tube. Subtract the background count from each of the readings. Place counts per minute on the vertical axis and the distance on the horizontal axis. Describe the relationship between distance and counts per minute.

   The graph shows an inverse relationship.

2. **Organizing Data** On a separate piece of graph paper, plot a graph of the number of index cards versus counts per minute. Place the counts per minute on the vertical axis. Describe the relationship between the number of index cards and counts per minute.

   The graph shows an inverse relationship.

3. **Organizing Data** On a separate piece of graph paper, plot a graph of the number of sheets of aluminum foil versus counts per minute. Place the counts per minute on the vertical axis. Describe the relationship between the number of sheets of aluminum and counts per minute.

   The graph shows an inverse relationship.

Radioactivity *continued*

Conclusions

1. Analyzing Results According to the three graphs, which substance is the most efficient absorber of beta particles? Explain how you made your decision.

Aluminum; the slope of the line is the least when aluminum foil is used.

2. Relating Ideas What is the implication of discovering a larger-than-normal amount of helium in a natural-gas well?

A higher concentration of helium in natural gas could mean that there is a

higher-than-normal concentration of radioactive material in that location.

Detecting Radioactivity

Teacher Notes

TIME REQUIRED Two 45-minute lab periods (with exposure time of 3 weeks—can be shortened with a source of alpha particles)

SKILLS ACQUIRED

Collecting data
Communicating
Designing experiments
Inferring
Interpreting
Measuring
Organizing and analyzing data

RATING

Easy ◄——— 1   2   3   4 ———► Hard

Teacher Prep–3
Student Set-Up–3
Concept Level–3
Clean Up–3

THE SCIENTIFIC METHOD

Make Observations Students build a radon detector and observe the tracks of alpha particles

Test the Hypothesis Conclusions questions 2 and 3

Analyze the Results Analysis questions 1 to 7

Draw Conclusions Conclusions question 1

Communicate the Results Analysis questions 1 to 7 and Conclusion question 1

MATERIALS

For teacher use only

- 10 mL, 6.25 M NaOH, per lab group

- 1000 mL beaker or 400 mL beakers, 2

- Bunsen burner or hot plate

- small test tube, 1 per lab group

To prepare 1 L of 6.25 M NaOH, observe the required safety precautions. Slowly and with stirring, dissolve 250.0 g of NaOH in 750 mL of distilled water. Then, after the solution has cooled, add enough distilled water to make 1 L of solution. The NaOH solution will get hot as the pellets dissolve. To prevent boiling and splattering, add the pellets a few at a time with stirring.

An empty film canister can be used in place of the small plastic cup with lid.

CR-39 plastic is available from Alpha Trak, 141 Northridge Drive, Centralia, WA 98531, (206) 736-3884.

SAFETY CAUTIONS

Read all safety cautions, and discuss them with your students.

Students should not handle NaOH solutions with concentrations greater than 1.0 M.

Wear safety goggles, a face shield, impermeable gloves, and a lab apron when you prepare and use the 6.25 M NaOH for the etching step. Work in a hood known to be in operating condition and have another person present nearby to call for help in case of an emergency. Be sure you are within a 30 s walk of a safety shower and eyewash station known to be in good operating condition.

If students observe the etching process, they should wear safety goggles, a face shield, and a lab apron, and they should stand at least 5 ft from the caustic solution.

If students use radioactive sources, they must wear impermeable disposable gloves when handling these objects. "One-size-fits-all" polyethylene gloves are available at most grocery stores. The gloves should be removed by turning them inside out as they are taken off the hand and fingers. Keep them inside out when disposing of them in the trash can.

In case of a NaOH spill, first dilute with water. Then mop up the spill with wet cloths or a wet cloth mop while wearing disposable plastic gloves.

Remind students of the following safety precautions:

- Always wear safety goggles and a lab apron to protect your eyes and clothing. If you get a chemical in your eyes, immediately flush the chemical out at the eyewash station while calling to your teacher. Know the location of the emergency lab shower and the eyewash stations and procedures for using them.

- Do not touch any chemicals. If you get a chemical on your skin or clothing, wash the chemical off at the sink while calling to your teacher. Make sure you carefully read the labels and follow the precautions on all containers of chemicals that you use. If there are no precautions stated on the label, ask your teacher what precautions you should follow. Do not taste any chemicals or items used in the laboratory. Never return leftovers to their original containers; take only small amounts to avoid wasting supplies.

- Call your teacher in the event of a spill. Spills should be cleaned up promptly, according to your teacher's directions.

- Never put broken glass in a regular waste container. Broken glass should be disposed of properly.

- Scissors and push pins are sharp; use with care.

DISPOSAL

Neutralize waste NaOH solution by adding 1.0 M acid slowly, while stirring, until the pH is between 5 and 9. After checking that the pH is in this neutral range, the solution may be poured down the drain. Save the etched plastic for examination by students next year.

TECHNIQUES TO DEMONSTRATE

Either demonstrate how to build the detector, or have one on hand for students to examine.

You should not need to explain the usage of the microscope, but students will need help measuring and calculating the field of view. Also be certain that they focus the microscope on the proper level of the plastic.

TIPS AND TRICKS

If students observe the etching process, they should wear safety goggles, a face shield, and a lab apron, and they should stand at least 5 ft from the caustic solution.

Pour enough 6.25 M NaOH into each test tube so that the plastic will be completely immersed when the paper clip is hooked over the test tube's edge.

Check the paper clip and etch clamp to be certain the students have attached them properly to the CR-39 plastic.

Hook the paper clip over the test tube lip so that the CR-39 plastic is completely immersed in the NaOH.

Add water to the beaker(s). Place the test tubes in the water.

Heat the water bath to boiling, and boil for about 30 min. The water may have to be replenished periodically.

Carefully remove the CR-39 from the hot-water bath, and rinse it thoroughly. Dry the plastic with a soft tissue.

Thoroughly discuss all safety precautions outlined in this laboratory and in the safety section. Radioactivity is a poorly understood topic, so take this opportunity to discuss practical ways to reduce exposure.

Discuss how the properties of radon as a gas cause problems in airtight buildings.

Explain that the CR-39 plastic is covered with the polyethylene tape to protect it from radiation until it is ready for use. The NaOH bath strips away a thin layer of the plastic to expose the pathway of the alpha particles.

Discuss the calculations for Bq/L before the students make the calculations themselves. They often do not realize that $activity = 2373$ tracks/cm^2/day was determined as a standard from 370 pCi/L of air (13.69 Bq/L). The standard was used to calculate unknown concentrations of radon.

Skills Practice

Detecting Radioactivity

The element radon is the product of the radioactive decay of uranium. The $^{222}_{86}$Rn nucleus is unstable and has a half-life of about 4 days. Radon decays by giving off alpha particles (helium nuclei) and beta particles (electrons) according to the equations below, with $^4_2$He indicating an alpha particle and $^{\ 0}_{-1}\beta$ representing a beta particle. Chemically, radon is a noble gas. Other noble gases can be inhaled without causing damage to the lungs because these gases are not radioactive. When radon is inhaled, however, it can rapidly decay into polonium, lead, and bismuth, all of which are solids that can lodge in body tissues and continue to decay. The lead isotope shown at the end of the chain of reactions, $^{210}_{82}$Pb, has a half-life of 22.6 years, and it will eventually undergo even more decay before creating the final stable product, $^{206}_{82}$Pb.

$$^{222}_{86}\text{Rn}$$
$$\searrow$$
$$^{218}_{84}\text{Po} + ^4_2\text{He}$$
$$\searrow$$
$$^{214}_{82}\text{Pb} + ^4_2\text{He}$$
$$\searrow$$
$$^{214}_{83}\text{Bi} + ^{\ 0}_{-1}e$$
$$\searrow$$
$$^{214}_{84}\text{Po} + ^{\ 0}_{-1}e$$
$$\searrow$$
$$^{210}_{82}\text{Pb} + ^4_2\text{He} \rightarrow$$

In this experiment, you will measure the level of radon emissions in your community. First you will construct a simple detector using plastic (CR-39) that is sensitive to alpha particles. You will place the detector in your home or somewhere in your community for a 3 week period. Then, in the lab, the plastic will be etched with sodium hydroxide to make the tracks of the alpha particles visible. You will examine the tracks to determine the number of tracks per cm^2 per day and the activity of radon at the location. Finally, all class data will be pooled to make a map showing radon activity throughout your community.

OBJECTIVES

Build a radon detector and use it to detect radon emissions.

Observe the tracks of alpha particles microscopically and count them.

Calculate the activity of radon.

Evaluate radon activity over a large area using class data and draw a map of its activity.

| Detecting Radioactivity *continued*

MATERIALS

- clear plastic ruler or stage micrometer
- CR-39 plastic
- etch clamp (the ring from a key chain)
- index card, 3 in. × 5 in.
- microscope
- paper clips
- push pin
- scissors

- small plastic cup with lid
- tape
- toilet paper or other tissue

Optional

- sources of radiation (Fiestaware, Coleman green-label lantern mantles, old glow-in-the-dark clock or watch faces, cloud-chamber needles)

 Always wear safety goggles and a lab apron to protect your eyes and clothing. If you get a chemical in your eyes, immediately flush the chemical out at the eyewash station while calling to your teacher. Know the location of the emergency lab shower and eyewash station and the procedures for using them.

Scissors and push pins are sharp; use with care.

Procedure

PART 1–DETECTOR CONSTRUCTION

1. Put on safety goggles, gloves, and lab apron.

2. Cut a rectangle, 2 cm × 4 cm, from the index card.

3. Locate the side of the CR-39 plastic that has the felt-tip marker lines on it. Peel off the polyethylene film, and use the push pin to inscribe a number or other identification near the edge of the piece. With a short piece of transparent tape, form a loop with the sticky side out. Place the tape on the back of the piece of CR-39 plastic (the side that is still covered with polyethylene), and firmly attach it to the index-card rectangle.

4. With a permanent marker, write the ID number or other identification on the outside of the plastic cup. Place the paper rectangle, with the CR-39 plastic on top, into the cup.

5. Cut a hole in the center of the plastic-cup lid. Place a small piece of tissue over the top of the cup to serve as a dust filter. Then snap the lid onto the cup.

6. Place the completed detector in the location of your choice. (Check with your teacher first.) Record this information in **Table 1.** The detector must remain undisturbed at that location for at least 3 weeks.

7. At the end of the 3 weeks, return the entire detector to your teacher for the chemical-etching process and the counting of the radiation tracks.

Detecting Radioactivity *continued*

PART 2–ETCHING

8. Remove the CR-39 plastic from the plastic cup, detach it from the index card, and peel the polyethylene film from the back. Slip the ring of an etch clamp over the top of the CR-39 plastic, and hook it onto a large paper clip that has been reshaped to have "hooks" at each end, as shown in **Figure 1.**

9. When you have completed this work, give the plastic to your teacher for the etching step. During this step, NaOH solution will be used to remove the outer layer of the plastic so that the tracks of the alpha particles become visible.

PART 3–COUNTING THE TRACKS

10. Examine **Figure 2** below. Notice the various shapes of the tracks left as alpha particles entered the CR-39 plastic. The circular tracks were formed by alpha particles that entered straight on, and the teardrop-shaped tracks were formed by alpha particles that entered at an angle.

Figure 1

11. Place your plastic sample under a microscope to view the tracks. Use a clear-plastic metric ruler or a stage micrometer to measure the diameter of the microscope's field of view. Make this measurement for low power (10×). Record this diameter in **Table 1.**

12. The tracks are on the top surface of the CR-39 plastic. Make certain that you focus on that surface and the tracks look like those in the illustration. These tracks were produced by placing the CR-39 plastic within a radium-coated clay urn. Your radon detector should not have nearly as many tracks. If there are too many tracks, switch to a high-power (40×) objective, and measure and record the diameter of the field of view. Place your piece of CR-39 plastic on a microscope slide. Count and record the number of tracks in 10 different fields. Record these numbers in **Table 2.**

Figure 2

Alpha particle tracks

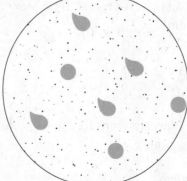

| Detecting Radioactivity *continued*

TABLE 1 DETECTOR TIME AND LOCATION DATA

Date detector was put in place	12/3/04
Time detector was put in place	3:45 PM
Location of detector (e.g., bedroom, kitchen, dining room, furnace room, under the stairwell, etc.)	kitchen
Floor level of location	1st
Date detector was removed	12/27/04
Time detector was removed	8:15 PM
Diameter of microscope field	Data will vary.

TABLE 2 ALPHA PARTICLE TRACK DATA

Field	1	2	3	4	5	6	7	8	9	10
Number of tracks	3	4	4	5	9	7	4	3	8	6

Analysis

1. **Organizing Data** In order to increase the accuracy of your data, you counted tracks in 10 different areas. Find the average number of tracks in a single area for your piece of CR-39 plastic.

$$\frac{3 + 4 + 4 + 5 + 9 + 7 + 4 + 3 + 8 + 6}{10 \text{ fields}} = 5.3 \text{ tracks/field on average}$$

2. **Organizing Data** You counted the number of tracks within the field of view of your microscope. In order to calculate the number of tracks per cm^2, you need to know the area of the field. Use the diameter of the field to calculate the area. (Hint: The field is circular; $d = 2r$; $A = \pi r^2$.)

$$A = \pi r^2 = (3.14)\left(\frac{0.17 \text{ cm}}{2}\right)^2 = 2.3 \times 10^{-2} \text{ cm}^2$$

3. **Organizing Data** Using the answers to Analysis items **1** and **2**, calculate the average number of tracks per cm^2.

$$\frac{5.3 \text{ tracks}}{0.023 \text{ cm}^2} = 230 \text{ tracks/cm}^2$$

▌Detecting Radioactivity *continued*

4. Organizing Data In Analysis item **3** you calculated the number of tracks that accumulated per cm^2 over the total period the detector was in place. Divide this number by the number of days the detector was in place to calculate tracks/cm^2/day.

$$\frac{230 \text{ tracks/cm}^2}{24.19 \text{ days}} = 9.5 \text{ tracks/cm}^2/\text{day}$$

5. Organizing Data Several pieces of CR-39 plastic were sent to a facility that had a radon chamber in which the activity of the radon was known to be 13.69 Bq/L (becquerels per liter of air), as measured by a different technique. A becquerel is the name for the SI unit of activity for a radioactive substance and is equal to 1 decay/s. The exposed pieces of CR-39 plastic were etched, counted, and found to have an activity of 2370 tracks/cm^2/day. Calculate the radon activity measured by your detector in becquerels/liter. (Hint: Use the proportion 13.69 Bq/L:2370 tracks/cm^2/day as a conversion factor to convert your data.)

$$9.5 \text{ tracks/cm}^2/\text{day} \times \frac{13.69 \text{ Bq/L}}{2373 \text{ tracks/cm}^2/\text{day}} = 5.5 \times 10^{-2} \text{ Bq/L}$$

6. Relating Ideas The Environmental Protection Agency and other U.S. government agencies use non-SI units of picocuries per liter (pCi/L) to measure radiation. One curie is 3.7×10^{10} Bq, and one picocurie is 10^{-12} curies. Convert your data into units of pCi/L.

$$5.5 \times 10^{-2} \text{ Bq/L} \times \frac{1 \text{ Ci}}{3.7 \times 10^{10} \text{ Bq}} \times \frac{10^{12} \text{ pCi}}{1 \text{ Ci}} = 1.5 \text{ pCi/L}$$

7. Organizing Data Combine your data with those of other teams in your class, and jointly construct a map of your region that shows the levels of radon activity in Bq/L and pCi/L at various locations throughout your community.

Student answers will vary.

▌Detecting Radioactivity *continued*

Conclusions

1. **Applying Ideas** The half-life of $^{222}_{86}$Rn is 3.823 days. After what time will only one-fourth of a given amount of radon remain?

   One-fourth will remain after 2 half-lives, 7.646 days.

   _____

   _____

   _____

2. **Designing Experiments** Factors other than geographic location can have an effect on radon emissions. For example, readings taken in basements are likely to be higher than those in attics. Design an experiment to test different aspects of the three highest and three lowest regions of radiation on the map to examine the influence of these other factors. If your teacher approves your suggestion, try it.

   Students' suggestions will vary. Be sure that student plans meet all neces-

   sary safety guidelines before allowing students to try them.

   _____

   _____

3. **Designing Experiments** CR-39 plastic could be used for further investigations of naturally occurring radiation. Design an experiment to explore one of the following areas. If your teacher approves your plan, carry out the experiment.

   • the range of alpha particles

   • the radon activity in soil

   • radioactivity of common items such as lantern mantles (Coleman green label), glow-in-the-dark clock or watch faces, and pieces of Fiestaware

   Students' suggestions will vary. Be sure that student plans meet all neces-

   sary safety guidelines before allowing students to try them.

   _____

   _____

   _____

Carbon

Teacher Notes

TIME REQUIRED 60 minutes, if the carbon models are made as a demonstration

SKILLS ACQUIRED
Collecting data
Communicating
Constructing models
Experimenting
Inferring
Interpreting
Organizing and analyzing data

RATING

Easy ◄——— 1   2   3   4 ———► Hard

Teacher Prep–3
Student Set-Up–3
Concept Level–3
Clean Up–2

THE SCIENTIFIC METHOD

Make Observations Students collect data on the properties of carbon.

Analyze the Results Analysis questions 1 and 2 and Conclusions question 1

Draw Conclusions Analysis question 1 and Conclusions questions 1 and 2

Communicate the Results Analysis question 2 and Conclusions question 1

MATERIALS

To prepare 1 L of 1.0 M hydrochloric acid, observe the required safety precautions. Slowly and with stirring, add 86 mL of concentrated HCl to enough distilled water to make 1 L of solution.

To prepare 1 L of 1.0 M sodium hydroxide solution, observe the required safety precautions. Slowly and with stirring, add 40 g of NaOH to enough distilled water to make 1 L of solution.

To prepare 1 L of dark-brown sugar solution, add 5 g of dark-brown sugar to enough water to make 1 L of solution.

To prepare 1 L of limewater, add 5 g of $Ca(OH)_2$ to 1 L of distilled water. Shake well and allow the undissolved solids to settle. Decant the saturated solution into another bottle.

SAFETY CAUTIONS

Wear safety goggles, a face shield, impermeable gloves, and a lab apron when you prepare the 1.0 M HCl and the 1.0 M NaOH. When making the HCl solution, work in a hood known to be in operating condition and have another person stand by to call for help in case of an emergency. In case of a spill, use a dampened cloth or paper towels to mop up the spill. Then rinse the cloth in running water at the sink, wring it out until it is only damp, and put it in the trash. In the event of an acid or base spill, dilute with water first, and then proceed as described. Be sure you are within a 30 s walk of a safety shower and an eyewash station known to be in good operating condition.

Remind students of the following safety precautions:

- Always wear safety goggles, gloves, and a lab apron to protect your eyes and clothing. If you get a chemical in your eyes, immediately flush the chemical out at the eyewash station while calling to your teacher. Know the location of the emergency lab shower and the eyewash stations and procedures for using them.

- Do not touch any chemicals. If you get a chemical on your skin or clothing, wash the chemical off at the sink while calling to your teacher. Make sure you carefully read the labels and follow the precautions on all containers of chemicals that you use. If there are no precautions stated on the label, ask your teacher what precautions you should follow. Do not taste any chemicals or items used in the laboratory. Never return leftovers to their original containers; take only small amounts to avoid wasting supplies.

- Call your teacher in the event of a spill. Spills should be cleaned up promptly, according to your teacher's directions.

- When using a Bunsen burner, confine long hair and loose clothing. If your clothing catches on fire, WALK to the emergency lab shower and use it to put out the fire. Do not heat glassware that is broken, chipped, or cracked. Use tongs or a hot mitt to handle heated glassware and other equipment because hot glassware does not always look hot.

- In case of a spill, use a dampened cloth or paper towels to mop up the spill. Then rinse the cloth in running water at the sink and wring it out until it is only damp, and put it in the trash.

- Never put broken glass in a regular waste container. Broken glass should be disposed of properly.

DISPOSAL

Combine all the liquids. Adjust the pH to between 5 and 9 and pour down the drain. Collect all solids; ensure that there are no flames or burning embers, and put into the trash.

TIPS AND TRICKS

To save time, the models could be assembled in a demonstration.

Students should understand that incomplete combustion of carbon-containing substances results when not enough oxygen is available to form CO_2 with all of the carbon in the substance. Some of the carbon combines to form CO; some doesn't combine at all, and therefore elemental carbon is produced.

Name _____ Class _____ Date _____

Carbon

Carbon exhibits allotropy, the existence of an element in two or more forms in the same physical state. Diamond and graphite are carbon's two crystalline allotropic forms. They result from the different ways in which carbon atoms link to one another in the two forms. A diamond contains an enormous number of carbon atoms that form an extremely strong, tetrahedral network. In graphite, the carbon atoms are bonded in a hexagonal pattern and lie in planes.

Microscopic graphite structures are contained in the black residues known as amorphous carbons that are obtained by heating certain carbon substances. Examples of amorphous carbon include charcoal, coke, bone black, and lamp-black. The amorphous forms are produced by a variety of procedures, including destructive distillation and incomplete combustion. If a carbon-rich compound such as gasoline, C_8H_{18}, is burned completely, the only products will be carbon dioxide and water vapor.

$$2C_8H_{18}(l) + 25O_2(g) \rightarrow 16CO_2(g) + 18H_2O(g)$$

Unfortunately, most internal combustion engines that run on gasoline are far from perfect. Incomplete combustion often results in black smoke (partially burned hydrocarbons) and carbon monoxide in the exhaust gases.

Carbon is an important reducing agent. The uses of its different varieties are related to particular properties, including combustibility and adsorption.

OBJECTIVES

Construct models of diamond and graphite.

Compare the observed physical properties of amorphous carbon with its molecular structure.

Infer why activated carbon is a good adsorbing agent.

| Carbon *continued*

MATERIALS

- activated charcoal, (for decolorizing)
- balance
- beaker, 250 mL
- Bunsen burner and related equipment
- buret clamp
- charcoal wood splinters
- crucible and cover
- dark-brown sugar solution
- Erlenmeyer flask, 125 mL
- filter paper
- forceps
- funnel
- funnel rack
- graduated cylinder, 50 mL

- HCl, 1.0 M
- iron ring
- limewater
- molecular model kits (2)
- NaOH, 1.0 M
- pipe-stem triangle
- ring stand
- rubber stopper, solid No. 4
- rubber stoppers, solid No. 2 (5)
- sugar, white granular
- test tube, 13 mm × 100 mm
- test tube, 25 mm × 100 mm (6)
- test-tube holder
- wooden splints

Always wear safety goggles, gloves, and a lab apron to protect your eyes and clothing. If you get a chemical in your eyes, immediately flush the chemical out at the eyewash station while calling to your teacher. Know the location of the emergency lab shower and eyewash station and the procedures for using them.

Do not touch any chemicals. If you get a chemical on your skin or clothing, wash the chemical off at the sink while calling to your teacher. Make sure you carefully read the labels and follow the precautions on all containers of chemicals that you use. If there are no precautions stated on the label, ask your teacher what precautions to follow. Do not taste any chemicals or items used in the laboratory. Never return leftovers to their original container; take only small amounts to avoid wasting supplies.

Call your teacher in the event of a spill. Spills should be cleaned up promptly, according to your teacher's directions.

Acids and bases are corrosive. If an acid or base spills onto your skin or clothing, wash the area immediately with running water. Call your teacher in the event of an acid spill. Acid or base spills should be cleaned up promptly.

Do not heat glassware that is broken, chipped, or cracked. Use tongs or a hot mitt to handle heated glassware and other equipment because hot glassware does not always look hot.

Carbon *continued*

When using a Bunsen burner, confine long hair and loose clothing. If your clothing catches on fire, WALK to the emergency lab shower and use it to put out the fire.

   When heating a substance in a test tube, the mouth of the test tube should point away from where you and others are standing. Watch the test tube at all times to prevent the contents from boiling over.

 Never put broken glass in a regular waste container. Broken glass should be disposed of separately according to your teacher's instructions.

Procedure

1. Put on safety goggles, gloves, and a lab apron.

2. Use a molecular model kit to start on the construction of the graphite model by constructing two hexagons using only the short connectors. Recall that the distances between the centers of adjacent carbon atoms in a layer of graphite are identical (142 pm). With **Figure 1** as a guide, connect the two hexagons using the longer stick connectors to represent the distance between centers in adjacent layers (335 pm). Use the remaining carbon spheres to build up each layer. Two carbons in the first hexagons you constructed will be common to the newly constructed hexagons. Use long connectors as needed between the rest of the constructed layers.

Graphite

Figure 1

3. Use 20 spheres representing carbon atoms from the molecular model kit to construct a model of diamond. Connect the spheres by means of the short stick connectors in the arrangement of atoms shown in **Figure 2.** How many carbon atoms is each carbon bonded to in the hexagon layer of graphite? What is the nature of the bonding between layers in graphite? How many carbon atoms is each carbon bonded to in diamond? Which structure is more rigid?

Diamond

Figure 2

Observations:

Each carbon is bonded to three carbon atoms in the hexagon layer. The

layers are held together by weak dispersion forces. Carbon is bonded to four

other atoms in diamond. Diamond is the more rigid structure.

_____

_____

| Carbon *continued*

---

4. Ignite a wood splint in the burner flame. Note how it burns.

5. Break several splints and place the pieces in the bottom of a test tube. Clamp the test tube to the ring stand so that its mouth is slightly downward, as shown in **Figure 3.** Place a piece of paper on the table under the mouth of the test tube and heat the contents strongly until no more volatile matter is released.

Figure 3

6. Remove the residue from the test tube carefully. Describe all the products of the reaction you observed.

Observations:

Liquid droplets from the tube fall on the paper. The residue in the tube is

charcoal black.

_____

7. Using forceps, ignite one piece of the solid residue in the burner and observe how it burns.

Observations:

student observations

_____

_____

| Carbon *continued*

8. Pour one inch of limewater into a small test tube. Using forceps, ignite another piece of solid residue, and insert the ignited end into the test tube, holding it above the limewater. Remove the ignited piece. Immediately stopper and shake the test tube. If nothing happens to the limewater, repeat with another piece of ignited residue. What happens to the limewater? What does this indicate about the nature of the residue?

Observations:

The limewater turns cloudy, indicating the presence of CO_2 gas.

_____

_____

9. Conduct an experiment to show that sugar may be decomposed into carbon and water vapor. Place 2 g of sugar into a porcelain crucible and cover it. Set the crucible and contents in a pipe-stem triangle. Heat the sugar on a low flame.

Observations:

student observations

_____

_____

10. Using a test-tube holder, hold a test tube horizontally with its closed end in a yellow burner flame. What form of carbon is produced?

Observations:

Carbon black is deposited on the test tube.

_____

_____

11. Change to the blue flame and hold the test tube so that the black deposit is in the hottest part of the flame.

Observations:

The deposit is removed by the oxidizing blue flame.

_____

_____

CAUTION Be careful when handling the acids and bases in step 12. Avoid contact with skin and eyes. If any of these chemicals should spill on you, immediately flush the area with water and then notify your teacher.

12. Conduct experiments to determine the activity and solubility of wood char-coal splinters in dilute hydrochloric acid, water, and sodium hydroxide solution. Label each of three test tubes with the name of one of the test solutions and place 5 mL of the appropriate solution in the test tube. Place charcoal splints into each of the solutions. Stopper the test tubes and shake the contents. Describe your results. Dispose of the liquids and any pieces of charcoal as directed by your teacher.

Observations:

There was no evidence of reactions taking place in any of the solutions.

_____

_____

_____

_____

13. Pour 50 mL of dark-brown sugar solution into a 125 mL Erlenmeyer flask. Add 1 g of powdered activated charcoal and stopper the flask. Shake the mixture vigorously for 1 min.

14. Set up a funnel with filter paper, and filter the mixture. Pour the filtrate through the funnel a second time, and even a third time, if necessary, to remove the color from the sugar solution. Finally, compare the color of the filtrate with that of the original brown-sugar solution.

Observations:

The filtrate is colorless.

_____

15. Clean all apparatus and your lab station. Return equipment to its proper place. Dispose of chemicals and solutions in the containers designated by your teacher. Do not pour any chemicals down the drain or in the trash unless your teacher directs you to do so. Wash your hands thoroughly before you leave the lab and after all work is finished.

Carbon *continued*

Analysis

1. Inferring Conclusions Of what use is activated charcoal in water purification processes?

Charcoal removes objectionable color and odors from water.

2. Analyzing Information What is adsorption? Why are certain forms of charcoal good adsorbing agents?

Absorption is the concentration of a gas, liquid, or solid on the surface of a

liquid or solid with which it is in contact. Activated charcoal is prepared in

such a way that it has very large internal surface areas. This makes it an

efficient adsorbing agent.

Conclusions

1. Analyzing Results In this experiment you used several different methods to prepare samples of carbon. What properties do all of the samples have in common? How does the model you built in **step 2** explain these properties?

All samples are unreactive, black, and somewhat soft. Graphite is a network

structure and is arranged in layers.

2. Analyzing Ideas Automobile engineers use the ratio of carbon monoxide to carbon dioxide in exhaust gases as a measure of the efficiency of an engine. Which is better, a high ratio or a low ratio? Explain your answer. (Hint: Refer to the equation for the complete combustion of gasoline in the Introduction.)

A low ratio is better. The less carbon monoxide and the more carbon dioxide

in the exhaust, the more complete the combustion.

Polymers

Teacher Notes

TIME REQUIRED 60 min

SKILLS ACQUIRED
Collecting data
Communicating
Experimenting
Inferring
Interpreting
Organizing and analyzing data

RATING

Easy $\longleftarrow$ 1   2   3   4 $\longrightarrow$ Hard

Teacher Prep–4
Student Set-Up–3
Concept Level–3
Clean Up–2

THE SCIENTIFIC METHOD

Make Observations Students observe the properties of several polymers.

Analyze the Results Analysis questions 1 to 3

Draw Conclusions Conclusions questions 1 and 2

Communicate the Results Analysis questions 1 to 3 and Conclusions questions 1 and 2

MATERIALS

Break a foam cup into pieces or use foam packing "peanuts." One or two cups should be enough for a class.

To prepare 1 L of 4% polyvinyl alcohol, slowly add 40 g of solid polyvinyl alcohol to about 960 mL of water while stirring with a glass stirring rod. Then heat the mixture to about 70°C and continue stirring at this temperature for about an hour or until the solution is clear. Some chemical suppliers provide prepared solutions.

Sodium polyacrylate can be dispensed easily from small, well-labeled salt shakers. Avoid breathing the dust when filling the shakers, by wearing a dust mask. Also wear the dust mask when preparing the sodium borate solution. To dispose of the dust mask, wrap it in a dampened newspaper and put it into the trash.

To prepare 1 L of 4% sodium borate, dissolve 40 g of solid borax, $Na_2B_4O_7 \cdot 10H_2O$, in enough water to make 1 L of solution.

Polymers *continued*

SAFETY CAUTIONS

Read all safety precautions, and discuss them with your students.

• Safety goggles and a lab apron must be worn at all times.

• In case of a spill, use a dampened cloth or paper towels. Then rinse the cloth in running water at the sink, wring it out until it is only damp, and put it in the trash. In the event of an acid or base spill, dilute with water first, and then proceed as described above.

• Acetone is flammable. Make sure there are no flames or other sources of ignition present before using this chemical. Limit the amount of acetone in the laboratory to no more than 200 mL in two or more bottles, each containing no more than 100 mL.

• Contrary to common belief, borax is toxic. Do not allow students to handle borate polymer with bare hands. Do not allow students to take even a small sample of the borate polymer out of the lab.

TIPS AND TRICKS

Discuss the structures of the polymers given on the first page.

Remind students that they are seeing three-dimensional structures presented in two dimensions.

Encourage students to think about how the polymers might occupy space, given the tetrahedral orientation of bonds around each carbon.

DISPOSAL

Collect the acetone (if any), dilute it 20-fold with water, and pour it down the drain. Collect the foam-acetone pieces. In a hood known to be operating properly, let any residual acetone evaporate, and then put the remainder into the trash. All else can go directly into the trash.

Polymers

Polymers are giant molecules consisting of repeating monomers, which are groups of atoms that form chains that are thousands of atoms long. Because these long molecular chains are linked by intermolecular forces, they can be molded into useful objects. If short bridges of atoms form between long polymeric chains, the polymer is then said to be cross-linked. Cross-linking gives the polymer new properties. In this experiment, you will investigate the properties of polystyrene, polyvinyl alcohol, and sodium polyacrylate.

Intermolecular forces of attraction   **Cross-linking**   **Gel formation**

Polystyrene is not cross-linked, but its intermolecular forces of attraction make it useful for constructing products such as radio cases, toys, and lamps. When polystyrene is expanded to produce the material called plastic foam, it has a very low density and is used to make egg cartons, insulation, and fast-food containers. The intermolecular forces of attraction in polystyrene are destroyed by the action of acetone, and the polymer loses its shape and becomes fluid.

Polystyrene chain

| Polymers *continued*

Polyvinyl alcohol can be weakly cross-linked with the hydrated borate ion, $B(OH)_4$. This polymer forms a non-Newtonian gel, which has properties similar to the Slime toy manufactured by Mattel, Inc. When kept in motion, it forms a semi-rigid mass; when held steady, it flows.

Polyvinyl alcohol cross-linked with borate ion

Sodium polyacrylate is a strongly cross-linked polymer that has superabsorbent properties. It can form a gel by absorbing water that has as much as 800 times its own mass. Currently, it is used to coat seeds before planting and to remove water from diesel and aviation fuels. Some brands of disposable diapers contain this superabsorbent polymer.

OBJECTIVES

Infer chemical structures from differences in chemical properties.

Deduce the solubility of plastic foam.

Describe the properties of three polymers.

MATERIALS

- 4% polyvinyl alcohol
- 4% sodium borate solution
- 10 mL graduated cylinder
- 50 mL beaker
- 5 mL acetone
- foam (polystyrene) cup or foam packing peanuts
- glass stirring rod

- medicine dropper
- NaCl
- paper towel
- petri dish
- sodium polyacrylate
- spatula
- watch glass

Polymers *continued*

⚠️ 🧍 For this experiment, wear safety goggles, protective gloves, and a lab apron, to protect your eyes, hands, and clothing. If you get a chemical in your eyes, immediately flush the chemical out at the eyewash station while calling to your teacher. Know the locations of the emergency lab shower and the eyewash station and the procedures for using them.

☠️ Do not touch any chemicals used in the laboratory. If you get a chemical on your skin or clothing, wash the chemical off at the sink while calling to your teacher. Make sure you carefully read the labels and follow the precautions on all containers of chemicals that you use. If there are no precautions stated on the label, ask your teacher what precautions you should follow. Do not taste any chemicals or items used in the laboratory. Never return leftovers to their original containers; take only small amounts to avoid wasting supplies.

🔥 Call your teacher in the event of a spill. Spills should be cleaned up promptly, according to your teacher's directions.

🔨 Never put broken glass in a regular waste container. Broken glass should be disposed of properly.

Procedure

1. Measure 5 mL of acetone and pour it into a petri dish. Place two or three pieces of expanded polystyrene (foam) into the acetone. After a few minutes, examine the polystyrene.

Observations:

The foam cup pieces slowly lose their shape and settle into blobs. Packing

peanuts fizz and collapse into blobs.

2. Use a spatula to lift out the polystyrene pieces and place them onto a paper towel. Using a medicine dropper, place a few drops of acetone from the petri dish onto a watch glass and allow them to evaporate. Dispose of the remaining acetone in the metal safety can provided by your teacher. Additionally, place several drops of pure acetone onto a watch glass and allow them to evaporate.

Observations:

When the pure acetone evaporated, very little residue remained. When the

solvent from step 1 evaporated, a translucent film was observed.

Polymers *continued*

3. Pour 25 mL of 4% polyvinyl alcohol into a 50 mL beaker. Slowly stir in 3 mL of 4% sodium borate solution. Be sure you have your gloves on. Pour the gel onto your lab bench top. Pick up the gel and knead it into a ball. Pull it slowly, as shown in **Figure A.** Pull it quickly. Hold part of it in your hand over a beaker, and let the rest stretch downward.

Polymer

Figure A

Observations:

When pulled slowly or held steady, it flows, and when pulled quickly, it

breaks.

CAUTION Although sodium polyacrylate is nontoxic, it readily absorbs water. For this reason, its dust should not be inhaled.

4. Place two squares of paper towel, about 10 × 10 cm, on your lab bench, about 5 cm apart. Sprinkle the center of one of the paper towels with sodium polyacrylate polymer, as shown in **Figure B.** Cover each paper towel with a second paper towel.

Figure B

5. Slowly add 5 drops of water from a medicine dropper onto the center of the first pair of paper towels, and then slowly add 5 drops of water onto the center of the other pair. Repeat this procedure until one pair of the paper towels appears saturated with water. Remove the top paper towels and examine each bottom towel. Record your observations of the bottom paper towel.

Observations:

The towel with the polymer was dry. A colorless gel had formed. The

untreated paper towel was saturated with water.

| **Polymers** *continued* |

6. In the center of a clean petri dish lid, lightly sprinkle a few grains of sodium poly-acrylate polymer. Slowly add a few drops of water until a gel forms. Pause between each drop to see how your gel is growing. By repeating this process, form a tower of gel 2 cm high. Your tower may be more of a mound, depending on how the gel grows. Then sprinkle a few grains of salt onto the top, as shown in **Figure C.**

Figure C

Observations:

When salt is added, the gel becomes very fluid, and the tower or mound of

gel is destroyed.

DISPOSAL

7. Clean all apparatus and your lab station. Return equipment to its proper place. Dispose of chemicals and solutions in the containers designated by your teacher. Do not pour any chemicals down the drain or in the trash unless your teacher directs you to do so. Wash your hands thoroughly after all work is finished and before you leave the lab.

Analysis

1. Analyzing Results From your observations of the residue formed from the evaporated pure acetone and acetone from the petri dish, what can you conclude about the solubility of the foam in acetone?

Little residue was formed from the pure acetone. Some residue was observed

from the acetone used with the foam. Therefore, some foam dissolved in the

acetone.

2. Analyzing Results The slime that you prepared in step **3** stretches when pulled slowly, but it breaks when pulled quickly. How can you explain this behavior based on its structure?

Slow pulling permits time for the borate ion to form a cross-link at a new

location.

3. Analyzing Results Refer to the structures of the polymers, and explain why sodium polyacrylate can absorb large quantities of water but polystyrene cannot.

Sodium polyacrylate is strongly cross-linked with the borate ion. There are

internal spaces in the structure where water molecules can fit. Polystyrene

is not cross-linked, so it doesn't have spaces for absorbed water

Conclusions

1. Relating Ideas What is the advantage of coating a seed with sodium poly-acrylate polymer before planting?

This polymer facilitates seed germination by keeping the seed moist.

2. Relating Ideas The polymers you investigated in this lab are only a small fraction of the polymers you encounter every day. Natural polymers are found in your body, in the foods you eat, and in plant structures. Name some poly-mers that are familiar to you.

hair and skin, starches, and cellulose and lignin of plants

Measuring the Iron Content of Cereals

Teacher Notes

TIME REQUIRED Part 1, 45 min; Part 2, 15 min

SKILLS ACQUIRED

Collecting data
Communicating
Designing experiments
Experimenting
Inferring
Interpreting
Measuring
Organizing and analyzing data

RATING

Easy ← 1   2   3   4 → Hard

Teacher Prep–3
Student Set-Up–3
Concept Level–3
Clean Up–2

THE SCIENTIFIC METHOD

Make Observations Students collect data on the iron content of cereals.

Analyze the Results Analysis questions 1 to 5

Draw Conclusions Analysis questions 4 and 5 and Conclusions question 1

Communicate the Results Analysis questions 1 to 3

MATERIALS

Wear safety goggles, a face shield, impermeable gloves, and an apron when you prepare the hydrochloric acid, HCl, solution. Work under a chemical fume hood known to be in operating condition, and have another person stand by to call for help in case of an emergency. Be sure you are within a 30 s walk from a safety shower and an eyewash station known to be in good operating condition.

Prepare a 0.2% solution of HCl by diluting 0.2 mL of concentrated HCl to a final volume of 100 mL of water.

Choose cereals containing differing amounts of iron, such as the following: Total, MultiGrain Cheerios, Oatmeal Squares, and Product 19.

The balance used must allow the student to record mass to the milligram.

SAFETY CAUTIONS

Read all safety precautions, and discuss them with your students.

• Safety goggles and a lab apron must be worn at all times.

• In case of a spill, use a dampened cloth or paper towels to mop up the spill. Then rinse them in running water at the sink, wring them out until only damp, and put them in the trash.

TECHNIQUES TO DEMONSTRATE

Demonstrate the proper method for attaching the bar magnet to the stirring rod.

TIPS AND TRICKS

If a mortar and pestle are not available, place the cereal in a plastic bag and crush it with a rolling pin.

A magnetic stirrer and stirring bar may be substituted for the bar magnet. The magnetic stirrer gives better results.

You may want to vary this activity by mixing the crushed cereal and water in a sealed plastic bag. Place a large magnet on the outer surface of the bag. Iron particles will start to collect inside the bag, near the magnet.

Point out the location of the nutrition facts label on a cereal box. Discuss the content of the label, and make students aware that the numbers on this label are percentages, not masses. The RDA of iron is 18 mg for a 2000 cal diet.

DISPOSAL

Combine used and unused acid solutions in a large beaker. Adjust the pH with 1 M sodium hydroxide, NaOH, to between 4 and 7, then pour the mixture down the drain.

Skills Practice

Measuring the Iron Content of Cereals

All foods contain at least one of six basic nutrients essential for organisms to grow and function properly: carbohydrates, proteins, lipids, vitamins, minerals, and water. Few foods contain all six nutrients, and most foods contain a concentration of only one or two of these nutrients. But it is important that the foods we eat contain a combination of all six nutrients, so manufacturers fortify foods with additional vitamins and minerals. This is one way to ensure a properly balanced diet and to prevent nutritional deficiency diseases.

Flour and products made with flour were first fortified with iron in 1940. The human body requires iron for many functions. Most importantly, iron is used in the production of hemoglobin molecules in red blood cells. The iron contained in hemoglobin attracts oxygen molecules, allowing the blood cells to carry the iron throughout the body. Because red blood cells are being replaced constantly, there is a continuous need for iron in the diet. While an iron overdose is harmful and can cause kidney damage, iron deficiency can lead to anemia, a condition in which red blood cells cannot carry a sufficient amount of oxygen to cells. Iron is found in foods such as liver and other red meats, raisins, dried fruits, whole grain cereals, legumes, and oysters.

The nutritional content in packaged foods is listed on the nutrition facts label found on most food packages. The label provides a listing of all the nutrients, along with their recommended dietary allowances (RDAs) based on a 2000 calorie diet. The RDAs are the average daily amounts of various nutrients that, in the opinion of scientists, we should consume daily to remain healthy.

One staple breakfast food is cereal. Most brands provide a minimum of 25% of the RDA for iron. Typically, very tiny particles of pure, powdered metallic iron are mixed in the cereal batter along with other additives. When consumed, the iron particles react with the digestive juices in the stomach and change to a form easily absorbed by the human body. Acidic foods can actually increase iron absorption threefold to sevenfold.

In this investigation, you will isolate and quantify the amount of iron added to three breakfast cereals and compare the amount collected to the amount listed on each food label. In addition, you will simulate how an acidic environment in the stomach aids in the conversion of iron particles to a form easily absorbed in the body.

OBJECTIVES

Isolate and **measure** the iron content in breakfast cereals.

Compare the iron content listed on various cereal boxes to lab results.

Observe the action of acids on iron.

| Measuring the Iron Content of Cereals *continued*

MATERIALS

- 0.2% HCl
- cereals, 3 brands with high iron content, one serving of each
- 400 mL beakers, 3
- balance, graduated in centigrams
- strong bar magnet
- glass stirring rod
- wash bottle, containing deionized water
- magnetic stirrer and stirring bar (optional)
- magnifier (optional)
- mortar and pestle
- test tube
- transparent tape
- wax pencil
- weighing boat

Always wear safety goggles and a lab apron to protect your eyes and clothing. If you get a chemical in your eyes, immediately flush the chemical out at the eyewash station while calling to your teacher. Know the locations of the emergency lab shower and the eyewash station and the procedures for using them.

Do not touch any chemicals. If you get a chemical on your skin or clothing, wash the chemical off at the sink while calling to your teacher. Make sure you carefully read the labels and follow the precautions on all containers of chemicals that you use. If there are no precautions stated on the label, ask your teacher what precautions you should follow. Do not taste any chemicals or items used in the laboratory. Never return leftovers to their original containers; take only small amounts to avoid wasting supplies.

Call your teacher in the event of a spill. Spills should be cleaned up promptly, according to your teacher's directions.

Never put broken glass in a regular waste container. Broken glass should be disposed of properly.

Procedure

PART 1: ISOLATING IRON FROM BREAKFAST CEREALS

1. Record in the **Data Table** the name of each of three iron-fortified cereals. Read the nutrition facts label for each cereal to find the mass of one serving and the percentage of the RDA for iron that is in each serving. Record these measurements in the **Data Table.**

2. Use a wax pencil to label three beakers, each with the brand name of one of the cereals. Weigh one serving of each cereal and put each into its labeled beaker.

3. Use a mortar and pestle to grind a serving quantity of each cereal into a fine powder. Place each powdered cereal in the appropriately labeled beaker. Remember to *clean* the mortar and pestle *after each use.*

4. Determine the mass of a bar magnet to the nearest milligram, and record your results in the **Data Table.**

Measuring the Iron Content of Cereals *continued*

5. Tape a bar magnet to the end of a glass stirring rod, leaving most of the bar exposed.

6. Pour 300 mL of warm water into one of the three beakers. Continuously stir the powdered cereal with the bar magnet for 10–15 min. The longer the cereal solution is stirred, the more the tiny iron particles will precipitate out of it and attach to the magnet. About 30 min of stirring gives the best results.

7. Remove the magnet, gently rinse it with deionized water, and carefully drain any excess liquid from it. When the magnet is dry, determine the mass of the magnet and iron slivers to the nearest milligram. Record your results in the **Data Table** and on the chalkboard so that average class results can be determined.

8. Place your bar magnet on a paper towel. Use a magnifying lens to observe the tiny slivers of iron attached to the bottom of the magnet. Record your description of the iron slivers below. Then collect the iron slivers from the magnet and save them for step **9**. Repeat steps **4–7** for the remaining two cereals.

Observations:

Student answers will vary. Students should see dark slivers with some metal-

lic luster.

_____

_____

_____

PART 2: SIMULATING THE ABSORPTION OF IRON IN THE BODY

9. Combine in a test tube all of the iron slivers you collected.

10. Pour 5 mL of 0.2% HCl in the test tube, and let the iron slivers and HCl stand for 10 min. Record any change(s) in the color, shape, or size of the iron slivers.

Student answers will vary. Students should see a few bubbles.

_____

_____

_____

DISPOSAL

Clean all apparatus and your lab station. Return equipment to its proper place. Dispose of chemicals and solutions in the containers designated by your teacher. Do not pour any chemicals down the drain or put them in the trash unless your teacher directs you to do so. Wash your hands thoroughly after all work is finished and before you leave the lab.

Measuring the Iron Content of Cereals *continued*

Data Table

	Cereal A: MultiGrain Cheerios, 30 g		Cereal B: Total, 30 g		Cereal C: Quaker Oatmeal Squares, 56 g	
	Your result	Class average	Your result	Class average	Your result	Class average
Initial mass of magnet (g)	20.000		20.000		20.000	
Final mass of magnet (g)	20.016		20.018		20.014	
Mass of iron recovered (mg)	16		18		14	
Percentage of RDA for iron on the label	100%		100%		90%	
Accepted mass of iron (mg)	18		18		16.2	
Percentage error	11.1%		20%		13.6%	

Analysis

1. **Organizing Data** Calculate the mass of iron recovered from each cereal by subtracting the initial mass of the magnet from the final mass of the magnet. Record your answers in the **Data Table**.

   <u>Answers will vary depending on the cereals chosen and students' technique,</u>

   <u>but they should be less than the actual amounts expected from the RDA label.</u>

2. **Organizing Data** Calculate the accepted mass of iron in each cereal tested by multiplying the percentage from the nutrition facts label by 18 mg (the RDA for iron). Record your answers in the **Data Table**.

   <u>Answers will vary depending on cereal chosen. For MultiGrain Cheerios:</u>

   <u>100% × 18 mg = 18 mg</u>

3. **Organizing Data** To determine the percentage error for each iron measurement, subtract the mass of iron recovered from the accepted mass of iron. Then divide the difference by the accepted mass of iron, and multiply by 100%. Record your answers in the **Data Table**.

   For Cheerios: percentage error = $\dfrac{18 \text{ mg} - 16 \text{ mg}}{18 \text{ mg}} \times 100 = 11.1\%$

Measuring the Iron Content of Cereals *continued*

4. Applying Concepts A food label lists the serving amount of a particular food as providing 35% of the RDA of iron. If the RDA based on a 2000 Cal diet is 18 mg, what amount of iron must a person consume from other foods to get 100% of the recommended dietary allowance?

Because 35% of 18 mg is 6.3 mg, a person must consume an additional

11.7 mg of iron.

_____

5. Analyzing Data Examine your percentage error entries in the **Data Table.** How closely do your results verify the claims made by the cereal manufacturers? If your percentage errors are high, suggest reasons for this.

Accept all reasonable answers. Students' results should justify their

answers. Technique, strength of magnet, and experimental method are three

main sources of error.

5. Inferring Conclusions How do you think the iron isolated from cereal compares with the iron found in nails and bridges?

Student answers may vary. Both sources are metallic iron and are attracted

to magnets. They differ in form, purity, and particle size.

_____

Conclusions

1. Designing Experiments Use a metal file to scrape off metal flakes from a piece of iron metal or nail. Compare the size of the particles collected from this iron to the particle size collected from cereals.

The metal flakes will look similar, but the metal scrapings will be larger.

_____

_____